DATE		
NOV 18	OCT 28 1982	
FEB 5	MAY 13 A.M.	
DEC 17		
DEC 22 78		
JAN 31 79		
MAY 31 79		
MAR 28		

JAN 20

SEP 30 1982

THE STORY OF THE
FIRST WORLD WAR

AMERICAN MILITARY HISTORY SERIES

THE STORY OF THE REVOLUTIONARY WAR

THE STORY OF THE WAR OF 1812

THE STORY OF THE CIVIL WAR

THE STORY OF THE SPANISH-AMERICAN WAR

THE STORY OF THE FIRST WORLD WAR

THE STORY OF THE MEXICAN WAR

THE NORTHERN GENERALS

THE SOUTHERN GENERALS

CLINT LANE SERIES

WEST POINT PLEBE

WEST POINT YEARLING

WEST POINT SECOND CLASSMAN

WEST POINT FIRST CLASSMAN

SECOND LIEUTENANT CLINT LANE: WEST POINT TO BERLIN

CLINT LANE IN KOREA

OTHER BOOKS

WHISPERING WIND

THE SHERIFF OF HAT CREEK

ATTACK AT FORT LOOKOUT

POINTERS ON ATHLETICS

SHERIDAN: THE GENERAL WHO WASN'T AFRAID TO TAKE A CHANCE

BORN AT REVEILLE

ARMY BRAT

THE STORY OF THE FIRST WORLD WAR

by

COLONEL RED REEDER

DUELL, SLOAN AND PEARCE

New York

Second printing, August 1967

Affiliate of
MEREDITH PRESS
Des Moines & New York

Library of Congress Catalogue Card Number: 62-15474

MANUFACTURED IN THE UNITED STATES OF AMERICA FOR MEREDITH PRESS

VAN REES PRESS • NEW YORK

To

Russell Potter Reeder III
Private First Class, United States Army

CONTENTS

ILLUSTRATIONS
following page 22

Von Hindenburg, the Kaiser, Ludendorff
Joffre
Von Richthofen
The Czar and the Grand Duke
Gallipoli
Haig
Foch
The *Lusitania*
The *U-139*
Wilson
Camouflaged U.S. Ship
Pershing and Summerall
Billy Mitchell
Rickenbacker
American Tanks
Traffic Behind the Lines—Argonne
U.S. Coast Artillery
Russian Soldiers
Sergeant York
Lawrence of Arabia
Polar Bear Monument

MAPS

THE STORY OF THE
FIRST WORLD WAR

Chapter 1

THE LADIES FROM HELL

THE King's Own Scottish Borderers—the 7th Battalion—hiked along a country road. Each man thought of what awaited him at the trenches, or about his family at home. The trees of the French countryside were bright in their fall colors, but they did not rival the red, green, and yellow tartans of the bagpipers.

At a signal from the Pipe Major, the bagpipers shrilled out a wild tune. The Scots stepped out. The thud of their boots on the dirt road was a dull measure of the music. The leather straps of the packs did not bite as hard into their shoulders. The ancient tune made the Scotsmen think of the history of their regiment. The colors up front whipped in the breeze, and you could see the Sphinx on them. It represented service in Egypt in 1695. This was 1915. The First World War had been raging for over a year.

The Scottish regiments were nicknamed "The Ladies from Hell" because of their bravery in a fight and because some of them used to wear kilts. Now only their pipers wore them. The Borderers swung along to the tune. They seemed carefree for men heading for trenches and No Man's Land. But old-timers, like Piper Daniel Laidlaw, worried because there were numbers of recruits in ranks going into action for the first time.

When the pipers finished, the British band, marching behind, struck up a melody, and soldiers in the long column sang *It's a Long Way to Tipperary*. The song, written by a vaudeville composer, Jack Judge, reminded the men of home. That and its

robust tune explain its popularity as a marching song in World
War I.

The British regiment turned right in the center of a ruined
French town. The Scotsmen marched straight ahead. Both regi-
ments were approaching the trenches for a strike across No
Man's Land.

The Regimental Sergeant Major (RSM) of the Scots stepped
out of line and waited until the bagpipers marched by, then he
fell into step alongside the champion piper, Daniel Laidlaw.
Under his breath the RSM said to his friend, "I think half of our
laddies headin' into the trenches for the first time have knees o'
jelly. What d' ye think, Dan? Lookit the chap just behind."

Dan glanced at the eighteen-year-old Scot. There was no color
in the boy's face. He had a haunted look. His spirit seemed beaten
by his pack, his load of ammunition, his rifle, and the march toward the trenches.

At the halt to open tins of "bully beef" for supper, Piper Laidlaw walked along the column. The RSM was right: many of the
young soldiers looked frightened.

When the King's Own Scottish Borderers lined up in fours on
the road, ready to march, a single-seater Fokker monoplane
droned over the column two miles up. The plane was white. It
had three black Iron Crosses painted on its sides. The Scots gaped
at the plane. It was too high for their rifles.

"He's makin' a hundred miles an hour, so help me," a man said.

"Every bit of it," Piper Laidlaw observed.

Out of the south three "Tin Whistles" flew toward the white
plane. The German in the white plane, Oswald Boelcke, veered
toward the "Tin Whistles" of the Royal Flying Corps (RFC).
The planes roared over No Man's Land, a mile ahead.

When the planes were one hundred yards apart their machine
guns barked. Almost immediately, a British biplane caught fire.
It plummeted to earth, leaving a trail of black smoke.

The German plane zoomed upward as if pulled by a string. It
executed a loop, coming out of it underneath the two remaining
RFC "Tin Whistles." A machine gun cracked. Down went an-

other RFC biplane. The last "Tin Whistle" looked as if it were also hit. The plane lost speed. It sideslipped downward. The aviator fought to save himself. He was standing up, working at the controls, but he crashed not far from his two partners. Black smoke poured upward from the three wrecks.

Lieutenant Boelcke darted his white plane downward over the funeral pyres as if in salute to his enemies, then flew over the King's Own Borderers. Rifles blazed, but the plane banked, unharmed, and headed toward Germany.

The Borderers walked on in silence, every man in counsel with his thoughts. The defeat of the three RFC planes seemed an ill omen. A Scotsman at the front of the column sang the opening lines of the ballad, "Lang Johnny More," but the colonel, a few feet away, stopped him so that he could hear a British military policeman standing in the road.

"They are shelling the crossroad 'alf a mile ahead," the policeman said. "The general orders all troops to take to the fields, sir."

It was hard walking in the fields. German artillery thundered on the crossroad. Its accuracy was amazing. The road junction was bathed in iron.

Piper Laidlaw, marching behind the colors, studied the mottoes embroidered on them in gold thread. He liked the one, "Unless God be with us all is in vain."

When darkness came, the Borderers were guided into the trenches by British "Tommies"—soldiers. The smell in places was almost overpowering. It was a stench of blood-soaked mud, of decay, and of human refuse. Duckboards covered many of the mud holes, but there were stretches where there were no boards and where the mud was shoe-top deep.

The British regiment the Scots were relieving filed out through a communication trench, happy to go back for a rest after living in the narrow, seven-foot-high trenches for a month. A few British officers and noncommissioned officers stayed behind to make sure the Scotsmen were acquainted with the scheme of the trenches.

The dugouts smelled foul. The lantern in each cavelike, dank room emphasized the gloominess. At midnight German and Allied artillery duelled. Each side sent up greenish-white flares to see if the other side was attacking. The weird lights cast eerie glints on the cruel barbed-wire entanglements, a few yards out in No Man's Land. The bombardment sounded like thunder. Only men with nerves of iron could sleep.

At daybreak, the recruits of the Borderers stood on the fire steps and gazed through rows and rows of barbed wire into No Man's Land. The area had been a mining district, and a quarter of a mile ahead stood the ruins of a miners' town. A dead horse and two dead cows lay fifty yards from the trench, their feet pointing upward. Off to the right was Hill 70, part of it an ugly slag heap. The murky sky made the view seem even drearier than it was.

Officers visited their squads to make certain that each Borderer understood what was expected of him on the morrow. "We go over the top at five in the morn," they said. "First there'll be a braw and able bombardment on the Huns' trenches to chew up their wire, wreck their machine guns, and do in their bomb-proofs. The Huns will catch it heavy. We'll hurry through the lanes in our barbed wire. Compass direction, seventy-five degrees. Then remember to guide on that wreck of a town. It's name is Loos. The French attack with us—on the right. You'd like to go home, wouldn't you? If we do our job and break through the German lines, this attack could end the war."

The last sentence sent hopes high. The veteran soldiers felt they had been living charmed lives. "We want to go home before they send over a bullet with our name on it," they liked to say. The younger Borderers felt nervous—some of them, afraid.

The day dragged, and the night was worse. Men scribbled "last letters" home. A half-hour after dark there was a brisk fight when a German platoon came over, raided the trench, captured two Scotsmen, and hurried back.

"They'll know now that fresh meat is in the line," a Scotsman mourned. "They'll learn we are about to attack."

At five minutes to one in the morning, Allied artillery started pounding the German trenches. The din was fearful. It was hard to hear one's talk.

At three thirty, cooks' helpers carried a tub of mutton stew garnished with canned green peas and a huge graniteware teapot along the trench. Piper Laidlaw heaped his tin mess plate with the brown stew and filled his tin cup with tea. He noticed that recruits nearby were not eating. "If you don't fancy stew," Dan Laidlaw said, "pour yourself some tea. Good for what ails you."

Thirty minutes to go. In the eerie light of flares Piper Laidlaw could see recruits cringing against the front of the trench. German shells pounded the ground just ahead. Other shells, bursting in the air, sprayed iron fragments over the trench. One man was wounded in the neck. The crack of the shells sounded fearful.

Suddenly, the gas alarm rang. The Borderer on duty as gas sentry at the bell fell unconscious. The Scotsmen fumbled into their gas masks. A man sprang to put a mask on the fallen sentry. The clammy masks made breathing hard. Greenish-yellow chlorine gas from artillery shells filled the trench.

Piper Laidlaw noticed that a breeze was beginning to carry the gas away. Fifteen minutes to go, his watch said. He whipped off his mask. He placed his bagpipes on top of the trench and leaped up. Quickly he warmed up the pipes. The low wail greeted the men as he patted the bag.

When the pipes were warm, Laidlaw marched up and down along the top of the trench, playing the skirling march "Blue Bonnets Over the Border." The music screeched. It was weird, but comforting. It was the kind of music that had inspired fighting Scotsmen since ancient days.

The sunrise illuminated Laidlaw's kilt of Royal Stewart tartan and the plaid and thistle banner swinging from the bagpipes. In the top of the stocking of his right leg was the traditional small knife. The piper was a jaunty figure: red garter-flashes, bonnet with red toorie at a rakish angle. No dish-shaped steel helmet for Piper Laidlaw.

A German machine gun opened up. Bullets whipcracked over the trench. None hit Dan Laidlaw. His pipes now sobbed out the challenging "Highland Laddie."

The recruits were amazed that the bullets zipping over the trench did not hit the piper. Perhaps the aim of the Germans was high. The music thrilled them. The Borderers yanked off their masks and gripped their rifles. When the officers blew their whistles, every Scotsman leaped from the fire step—"over the top."

Laidlaw followed his platoon sergeant through the winding lane in the barbed wire, his pipes wailing, at the front of the skirmish line.

The Borderers headed for the German trenches five hundred yards away, bayonets fixed.

Laidlaw's pipes stopped suddenly. A bullet from a machine gun in a concrete pillbox had knocked him down. Another shot smashed his pipes, but the Borderers went on. Blood poured from the wound in Laidlaw's arm. His red face went white. His mustache seemed darker. In a few minutes two aid men placed him on a litter. "I'm well enough," Laidlaw whimpered. Then he added in a half-moan, "But I'll need new pipes."

Laidlaw was one of the first of the wounded to arrive at the aid station where Temporary Lieutenant George Mailing, surgeon of the Royal Medical Corps, worked. Soon Doctor Mailing had more patients than he had ever dreamed of. Three hundred lay about the aid station. There was no shelter. The more serious cases were screaming or unconscious.

The husky doctor went from patient to patient. He had started work at six fifteen. At eleven, a high explosive shell burst over the wounded, killing some, wounding Mailing's only assistant, and stunning the doctor. When Doctor Mailing was over the shock, he resumed his job. Another shell covered him and his instruments with dirt. He cleaned them and worked on, helping his patients. At night he tended them by the light of a coal-oil lamp. Doctor Mailing worked twenty-six hours at his aid station without relief.

The fierce attack of the Borderers and other British units pushed through Loos, but the Germans had three lines of trenches. The attack lasted for over a month, but it gained only two and one-half miles. The French and British in the south, up against Vimy Ridge, gained even less ground. The hope of breaking through into the open faded.

Months later Piper Laidlaw and Doctor Mailing stood at attention with other heroes before the King of England at a ceremony at Buckingham Palace. Citations were read describing the deeds of the men being honored. The King pinned the Victoria Cross to the coats of the heroes because of their personal bravery. The band played "God Save the King."

The attack at Loos and Vimy Ridge in northern France was in 1915.

The United States would also fight the Germans, but a year and eight months more would pass before United States soldiers in any number would be in France.

Chapter 2

WHAT CAUSED THE WAR?

T HE first of the world wars exploded in 1914. It was the worst war the world had ever seen. By the time it ended ten million people had been killed and double that number wounded.

The fighting spread over a large part of the earth: the British Isles, Belgium, France, Germany, Luxemburg, Italy, Austria, Greece, Russia, Turkey, Egypt, Mesopotamia and the deserts of the Holy Land, Africa, China, the high seas off every continent, and the nations of southeastern Europe now under the domination of the Soviet bloc. When the war started, this last group of nations was known as "the Balkans"; Austria was called "Austria-Hungary." [1]

When war clouds broke, in 1914, most Americans thought that the Atlantic would enable them to keep out of it. They were willing to sell supplies to all the nations involved, but they did not consider it their war. Few visualized that United States citizens would fight in France and on the oceans. But the United States entered the war after it had raged three years, and at the right hour to tip the balance in favor of the Allies.

To discover why the war was fought you must go back almost fifty years to another fateful year, 1870, for it was then that seeds of hatred were broadcast.

To a Frenchman, "1870" means the Franco-Prussian War.

[1] See Map No. 1, page 15.

Though it lasted only a year, it placed Germany as the leading nation on the continent of Europe. Two leaders gained victory for the Germans in that war, Count von Moltke, a military genius, and Otto von Bismarck, a giant whose drooping white mustache made him look like a walrus. Bismarck, nicknamed "The Iron Chancellor," was wise and crafty, but often unscrupulous. He wanted to unify Germany and make her all-powerful; he was determined to let nothing stand in his way. He even made friends with Russia, and this took some scheming.

Defeat in 1870 stunned France. Count von Moltke, the brains behind the German effort, captured the French Emperor and 104,000 of his men after the battle of Sedan, and another French army surrendered in the fortress at Metz. The Germans pressed on and surrounded Paris. After a long, bitter siege, the French army there became tired of fighting both famine and Germans, and surrendered. From then on the loss of the War of 1870 haunted France.

When the fighting stopped the Germans made the French swallow bitter pills. The rich mining and manufacturing area, Alsace-Lorraine, in eastern France, was taken by the Germans, and France was also made to pay one hundred million dollars to Germany.

France thirsted for revenge. Her leaders and her people worked hard. She rose to the position of the second most powerful nation on the Continent—second only to Germany.

But the Germans worked even harder. The German Army became the best in the world. The Germans overhauled their school system, their scientific research, and their methods of handling chemicals. Industry boomed. Soon German goods flooded every market.

The German Iron Chancellor resolved to force his country ahead. His method, and he was successful, was to play one nation against another. It seemed that as long as Otto von Bismarck lived there would be peace, but he suddenly lost his office. After twenty-eight years of service he was dismissed on short notice by the new German Kaiser, Wilhelm II.

The Kaiser was known by the diplomats of Europe to be vain, excitable, headstrong, and erratic. He had a withered arm and he was ashamed of it, but his courage enabled him to ride even a spirited horse. He was dangerous. The Kaiser fancied himself as the master diplomat of all time. Before the war he was jealous of his chancellor, Bismarck. The Kaiser wanted to rule, and he wanted no one telling him what to do.

To get Bismarck out of the way, the Kaiser made it appear that Bismarck had resigned. In truth, the Kaiser forced the retirement. The Kaiser's pettiness showed, too, because when he discharged Bismarck he said that Bismarck had been paid too much and must return eleven days' pay.

The Kaiser began to rule a booming nation. Germany's new industry called for raw materials and new markets, so she gained colonies of a million square miles in Africa and in the Pacific. The new colonies helped trade, but they called not only for a merchant fleet but for ships of war to protect the trade. Kaiser Wilhelm was equal to this, and gave Admiral von Tirpitz the job of building a fleet.

The Kaiser surrounded himself with advisors who flattered him and told him exactly what he wanted to hear. His word was law to generals, bankers, leaders of industry, scientists, judges, and many others. The Germans worshiped power, and the Kaiser was *the Power*. He said, "My trust is in my army," and he considered the army as his personally. Once when a colonel was reporting to him about stopping some trouble in a German colony in Africa, the colonel said, "I owe everything to my officers." The Kaiser shouted angrily, "Those are *my* officers!"

The relationship he claimed with God was peculiar. He said, "In everything I do I am carrying out the will of God," and "God is my ally."

When the Kaiser traveled about Germany he was received as though he were a savior. He wore shining breastplates on gaudy uniforms. A long white cloak concealed his withered arm. On his head was the spiked helmet of the German soldier, or a helmet supporting a silver eagle, or one topped with a tassel of white horsehair. His black, upturned mustache gave him a fierce look. He became the symbol of war. On maneuvers, when he played a general's part against another German general, he was allowed to win.

Because the Kaiser believed he could make no mistakes if war came, German generals worried—secretly. All important decisions were the Kaiser's to make. He told German soldiers that his word was law; that each soldier must be ready to fire on his own father and mother if he gave the order. Once when there was a political crisis in Germany, he went hunting. He wired his chancellor, who needed guidance, ... *The hunt went beautifully. I shot sixty-five stags.*

He was a troublemaker, and his belief that he was the world's greatest diplomat caused him to anger the British. When Britain was engaged in war against the Boers of South Africa, the Kaiser sent the Boer President Kruger a stupid telegram congratulating him on a victory. This was a slap in the face to the British, and it received wide publicity in Britain.

Admiral von Tirpitz carried out the Kaiser's orders and worked tirelessly to build the German Navy. When this navy had ships afloat, the Kaiser announced that his country was a world power, and this caused Great Britain to overhaul and enlarge her navy. When the Kaiser had enough battleships, cruisers, destroyers, and submarines for a review, he held one and invited his uncle, King Edward VII of England, to see it. The Kaiser was so blinded with vanity that he could not see this was a threat to the British. Nor could he see that he was making the British and the French allies. Both nations felt that, with Germany growing more and more powerful, they must team together in case of war.

Political leaders in England considered the rise of the German Navy a challenge, even though no nation had more steamships at sea than those under the British Union Jack. British naval leaders and statesmen decided to keep it that way. Arthur Balfour, a British statesman-politician, made an angry speech against Germany that frightened many of his own countrymen. The British people were warned of their danger. Other politicians notified them.

But the great masses of Englishmen were unconcerned. This was before TV and radio, and the press did not adequately inform the population. It seemed to many Englishmen to be more important to win at the horse races at Ascot or to have a good vacation than to worry about the Germans. The London magazine, *Punch*, did publish a cartoon that was widely circulated. It showed Kaiser Bill at the helm of the German ship with the pilot, Bismarck, being put ashore. But millions of Englishmen took this as just another joke about the Kaiser. They did not realize they were in grave danger.

But the Kaiser was not a villain to everyone. Feelings about him were divided in the United States. Most people in this country did not care what he did, nor did they worry about him. A few saw him as a threat to European peace. Another group believed him to be a marvelous leader. Pictures appeared in United States magazines and newspapers showing the beloved American President "Teddy" Roosevelt on horseback, riding with the Kaiser as guest of honor at a military review. Small boys in the United States wore bristling haircuts similar to the ones worn by German soldiers. Numerous American parents, whose own parents had come from Germany, or who liked the Kaiser, taught their sons to say, *"Hoch der Kaiser!"*—"Hooray for the Kaiser!"

England had other troubles. There was a strong movement for Home Rule in Ireland, but England was against that. In 1914 blood flowed in the streets of Dublin. However, when the first of the world wars started, the Irish stood by the British—although for only two years.

Things were in a mess in southeastern Europe in the small Balkan states.

Many of the small states hated and fought one another. On top of this, Turkey despised Russia. Austria-Hungary wished to expand toward the southeast and the Orient, but Russia

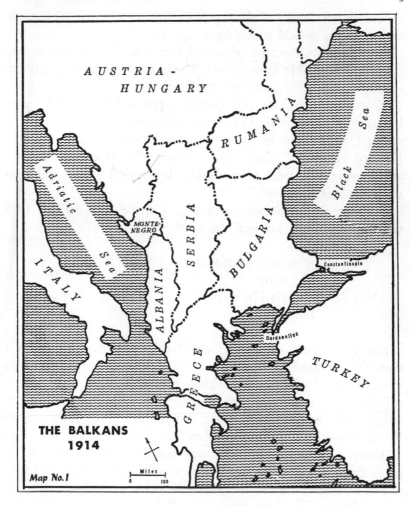

Map No.1 THE BALKANS 1914

blocked the way because the Russians themselves wanted to expand to the southwest and the Mediterranean Sea.

In the mixed-up boiling pot of the Balkans, Russia backed the Serbs, the most warlike of the Balkan people. Austria secretly decided to attack the Serbs, and the Serbs were attempting to organize revolts against the Austrians. The Italians were angry because the French had expanded in North Africa. European statesmen who knew of these political cross-currents and hatreds saw that war would probably come.

Sir Edward Grey, the powerful but scheming British statesman, stumbled. He encouraged Russia to build up its military machine, and this frightened the Germans.

Jealousies, ambitions and conflicts gradually turned Europe into a powder arsenal. Woodrow Wilson, who was President of the United States in 1914, started to worry. He sent Colonel Edward House, of Texas, abroad to see what could be done about preventing war. House said, "It requires only a spark to set the whole thing off."

By 1914 the principal nations of Europe had divided into two groups. They awaited the spark.

THE TRIPLE ALLIANCE	THE ALLIES
Germany	England
Austria-Hungary	France
Italy	Russia

But the largest of the Allies, Russia, was weak. Barbaric conditions existed in huge areas. The majority of her people were peasants who could neither read nor write. Her Czars ruled without regard for the common man. On top of this, the religion of the people was laced with fear and superstition. Russia was a land ripe for revolution.

About a month before the war Britain displayed her most powerful weapon when her Navy, supplied and ready to fight, passed in review before the King. This tremendous display of sea might gave the idea that Great Britain was ready to fight. The British Navy was ready, but the British Army was small and lacked certain modern weapons, such as heavy artillery.

In the United States, the great majority of the people failed to sense the coming tragedy. Life in our country flowed along, generally without trouble. Most Americans cared little about events in Europe. The average family was thinking of buying a car, or about the unusual World Series of 1914. Tales of hatreds and jealousies in Europe seemed like fairy stories, and when war started in 1914 most Americans were surprised.

In 1916 Americans had worries of their own south of the Rio Grande. When the Mexican President, Huerta, arrested a number of United States bluejackets at Vera Cruz, on the Gulf of Mexico, and failed to apologize properly, American marines and sailors captured the city. War between the United States and Mexico seemed likely.

But President Huerta resigned and war was averted. Then the colorful bandit and revolutionary leader, Pancho (Francisco) Villa broke loose. He and his cavalrymen dashed across the border and murdered Americans in New Mexico. American border towns were in danger. President Wilson, with the consent of the Mexican government, sent the United States Army into Mexico to hunt down the bandit. The expedition was commanded by Brigadier General "Black Jack" Pershing.

General Pershing and his men followed Pancho Villa into desert country. The bandit escaped, but his army fell apart. This was a small war, but the experience in Mexico and along the lonely miles of the Rio Grande helped the United States Army and the National Guard when they were tossed into the European cauldron.

When the world war started, the United States Navy was a splendid fleet, but the United States Army was scattered from Maine to the Philippines. It had many army posts, but only 24,000 soldiers who could move readily. The National Guard had 127,000 in varied degrees of training. Our air power consisted of twenty-one planes. The airplane was new, but not that new. France had 500 planes and eleven airships. A powder arsenal was about to blow up in Europe, inflaming the world, and the United States lacked a balanced force to protect its citizens and their commerce.

The spark igniting the First World War was supplied by a young Serb. He shot an Austrian archduke who was visiting in the Balkans. The archduke had on a white military jacket with two rows of gold buttons down the front. The bullets smashed a red pattern over the heart.

There was great excitement in Austria. The Austrians held Serbia responsible. Austria called her men to the colors and declared war on Serbia.

Russia got ready to fight. When news of the Russian preparations reached Germany, the Germans declared war on Russia, then on France. Country after country declared war. Europe went up in flames.

President Wilson announced that the United States would remain neutral.

Before the first of the world wars was over the fight involved 93 per cent of the world's population. There were fifty-nine declarations of war. The character of human life was changed. The world has never been the same since 1914. In one way or another the First World War affected almost every country and family on the entire globe.

Chapter 3

THE GERMAN WHEEL

WHEN war broke, the Germans were quick to act. Their armies were ready and waiting. Their generals had a secret plan by which they felt they could win the war in a hurry.

This plan had been worked out nine years before the start of World War I by Count von Schlieffen. It was daring and immoral. Immoral because it called for the German armies to smash through Belgium, a neutral country whose territory Germany was bound by treaty to respect.

When the Belgian King Albert was informed that the German armies were at his borders, he tried to stop them by writing his cousin, the Kaiser. Albert begged the Germans to renew expressions of friendship.

Back came the harsh German answer. It falsely accused Belgium. It said the Belgians were planning to help the French by permitting the French Army to march through Belgian territory and strike at Germany. The Kaiser promised that, if the Belgians did not hinder the march of the German armies through Belgium, the Germans would leave the country as soon as the war ended. The message also threatened, for it said that if Belgium were hostile the Germans would regard her as an enemy.

When King Albert saw the Kaiser's message he said, "It is war," and Belgium got ready to try to stop almost one million Germans.

The German plan was bold. It called for a quick defeat of the

French, then a shift of forces and attack on Russia. The planners hoped that the German armies on the western front would be able to finish off the French before the Russian hordes were ready to attack.

Four German armies would swing on great arcs through Belgium, flanked to the south by one more which would advance through northern France, just below the Belgian border. At the same time two other German armies would gain the attention of the French in eastern France near Alsace-Lorraine. The French would be lured to strike there, while the main blow against them would be the crushing enveloping movement—like a terrible scythe blade—swinging through Belgium and around Paris, catching the French Army in Alsace in the rear. The plan was crafty, because the harder the French attacked in Alsace-Lorraine the deeper they would fall into the German trap.

But the Kaiser's number-one general, Field Marshal von Moltke, was neither daring nor crafty. He looked more like a tired businessman than a venturesome general. He was not a man to take a chance. Von Moltke liked to temper decisions, balancing them, then hope for the best.

When the tall, striking-looking King of the Belgians saw that war could not be averted, he left his throne and took personal command of his army. He was a tragic figure, for he knew of the tremendous size and efficiency of the German armies. He appealed to England, France, and Russia for help.

The German minister told the British ambassador in Berlin that Germany's treaty with Belgium was "a mere scrap of paper." Civilized customs seemed to be ending.

While diplomats were talking about treaties and while armies were moving into position, a tragedy occurred. It cost three lives. To the soldiers of the German unit, it was a great loss, but in the light of the terrible events to follow, it was nothing.

Before the event happened, Oberleutnant Albert Mayer of the Light Mounted Infantry stood at attention at the head of his horse. In the soft, early morning light, the six German soldiers standing behind him looked like ghosts. Mayer's heart

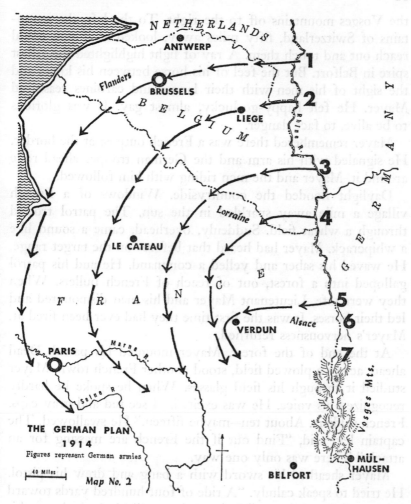

NETHERLANDS

ANTWERP

Flanders

BRUSSELS

B E L G I U M

LIEGE

1

2

Rhine R.

G E R M A N Y

3

Lorraine

4

LE CATEAU

F R A N C E

5

Alsace

6

VERDUN

Marne R.

PARIS

Seine R.

7

Vosges Mts.

THE GERMAN PLAN
1914

Figures represent German armies

40 Miles

Map No. 2

**MÜL-
HAUSEN**

BELFORT

beat fast. The longer he listened to his captain, the faster it pounded.

The captain finished, "... Find out, Mayer, if these rumors spread by peasants are true. I want to know if the French Army is massing across the border for attack. Any question?"

When Mayer and his six horsemen rode out of the village of Mülhausen, in Southwestern Germany, the sunrise was tinting the Vosges mountains off to the right. To the left, the mountains of Switzerland, fifty miles away, looked as if you could reach out and touch them. A ray of light highlighted the tallest spire in Belfort. But the feel of his horse between his knees and the sight of his men with their lances and carbines reassured Mayer. He felt happy-go-lucky, almost gay. It was glorious to be alive, to face danger.

Mayer remembered there was a French outpost at the border. He signaled with his arm and the German trooper ahead rode around it. Mayer and the men riding with him followed.

Daylight flooded the countryside. Windows of a French village a mile away sparkled in the sun. The patrol trotted through a wheat field. Suddenly, overhead, came a sound like a whipcrack. Mayer had heard that before—on the target range. He waved his saber and yelled a command. He and his patrol galloped into a forest, out of reach of French bullets. When they were safe, Lieutenant Mayer and his men dismounted and led their horses. It was the first time they had ever been fired at. Mayer's nervousness returned.

At the end of the forest, Mayer mounted his patrol. Dead ahead, across a plowed field, stood another French town. Mayer studied it through his field glasses. When he spoke he hardly recognized his voice. He was excited. "I see red and gray caps. French soldiers. About ten—maybe fifteen." He swallowed. The captain had said, "Find out if the French are massing for an attack." There was only one way.

Mayer sheathed his sword with a bang and drew his pistol. He tried to speak calmly. "A ride of four hundred yards toward that town. Fast trot until I signal. Lances." He looked over his group for the last time. "All right. Follow me."

Just as the first half of the field was covered, the French saw them. The Germans were bent low over the necks of their horses, lances extended. Mayer, on the fastest horse, galloped to the front. The wind tore at his face. His arm was thrust forward, his pistol cocked and ready.

Bullets whizzed overhead. As the German patrol raced from

General von Hindenburg, Kaiser Wilhelm, General Ludendorff.

Marshal Joffre.   Von Richthofen.

The Czar inspects; upper right, the Grand Duke. *Photographs top and center left National Archives, center right and bottom Culver Pictures, Inc.*

Horses picketed on beach—Gallipoli. *Imperial War Museum*

Field Marshal Haig.

Marshal Foch.

Culver Pictures, Inc.

Last trip of the *Lusitania*.

U-139–the sub that sank the *Lusitania*.

President Wilson (center) leads a parade.

Camouflaged U.S. ship.

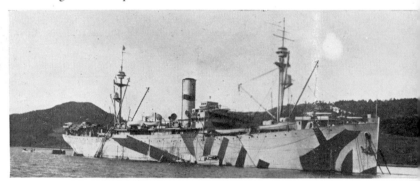

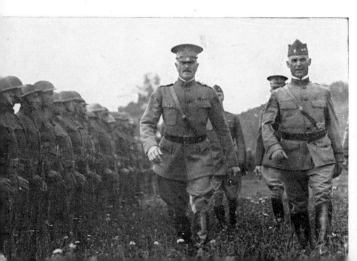

Generals Pershing and Summerall inspect 1st U.S. Division in France. *Photographs National Archive.*

Colonel Billy Mitchell and a two-seater Spad XVI.

Rickenbacker ready to take off in a Spad.

American tanks approach the Argonne.

Traffic behind the lines—Argonne.

Fourteen-inch railway gun
manned by U.S. Coast Ar-
tillery—Argonne.

Russian soldiers. *Culver Pictures, Inc.*

Sergeant York. Lawrence of Arabia.

Culver Pictures, Inc. *Imperial War Museum*

Polar Bear Monument, Detroit.

the field across a road, a French automatic rifle roared. Albert Mayer fell from his saddle. Two other Germans went down. With their leader killed, the mounted men wheeled and galloped for Germany. One German, who was shot in the shoulder, reeled, about to fall. A friend rode to the wounded soldier, put his arm about him, and supported him.

Back at the stable, the patrol obtained first aid for the wounded trooper and reported the death of Lieutenant Mayer and the two privates. "We saw only about thirty French," they said.

The French lifted Mayer's body and those of his two men. The entire town turned out to watch the military funeral given the three dead Germans. Later, when the Germans captured the town, they erected a monument over Mayer's grave. The inscription read:

LIEUTENANT ALBERT MAYER

JÄGER REGIMENT NUMBER 5

FIRST CASUALTY OF THE GREAT WAR

Two days after Mayer fell the Uhlans, German light cavalry, galloped across the Belgian border. The fateful day was August 4, 1914. World war was under way.

German siege guns bellowed and hurled projectiles weighing hundreds of pounds against the Belgian forts.

The Belgian Army of twenty regiments fought hard, but it was outnumbered, its equipment ancient. It had no heavy artillery. Dogs pulled machine gun and ammunition carts.

Worse, when King Albert called out the reserves, they hindered instead of helping. There was confusion. Some Belgian officers were overly enthusiastic and permitted parents to visit their sons on the outpost line, and this caused difficulty when the Germans struck. But the Belgians dug trenches between their forts and, for a while, offered hard resistance.

The Belgian border fortress and railroad center of Liége blocked the Germans. It was important to their scheme that their advance continue without delay. They could not bypass Liége.

They needed the railroad running through it to supply their armies when they were in France. *Nothing* could be allowed to stop the terrible wheel through the French countryside.

A tall, serious German, General Erich Ludendorff, now played a key role. When he saw that the first German attack on Liége had failed and that further attacks would cost precious time, Ludendorff commandeered a Belgian automobile and made its driver take him to the Belgian fort. The general jumped out and banged on the gate. He later wrote, "The doors opened from the inside. . . . I asked them to surrender and they did. It was a bold operation, the favorite recollection of my life."

But other Belgian forts and trenches held better than Liége. Tremendous German siege guns rolled into position. The cannonade against the Belgian Army echoed for miles, but some units held, slowing the German infantry. The fighting desolated the Belgian countryside. The ancient city of Louvain was set afire. Buildings there were soon gaunt shells. The famous Louvain cathedral and library were wrecked. Belgian Army units fought as best they could. King Albert's men, badly outnumbered, slowed the Germans when hours were valuable.

The German might swept on. Battalions of the Kaiser's soldiers snapped their legs out in a goose-step as they marched into Brussels, bands playing "Die Wacht am Rhein" and "Deutschland über Alles." Ahead of the infantry trotted the Death's Head Hussars, the noise of their horses' hoofs rattling on the cobblestones. There was panic as the population scurried for cover. Every shop in Brussels closed. For hours the Germans, in their horizon-gray uniforms and spiked helmets, poured into the capital. The Germans paused for ceremonies in the city square, then rushed on south toward France. They left many soldiers to keep order in Brussels.

While the Germans poured through Liége and Brussels, King Albert pulled back to the port of Antwerp. The Germans tried to cut off his army but could not.

The nervous and uncertain German general, von Moltke, now changed the plan for the first time. He took thousands of soldiers away from the German "wheel" to watch Albert's army.

But the Germans were confident as their long columns marched through the August heat. When they heard that the English had declared war on them and were sending a British Expeditionary Force to France, they laughed and said, "Let the little army come over. It will do it good to get licked."

Refugees clogged the roads. Grandfathers and grandmothers trudged alongside horse-drawn carts loaded with children and the best of the household goods. These were French and Belgians in the path of the war. They had one idea: to reach a place of safety. And where safety lay they did not know. Behind the refugees the guns rumbled in the distance. This sound scourged them on, no matter how tired they were. Once in a while Uhlans darted at the crawling columns, trying to clear the roads for German infantry.

French soldiers died trying to stop the German armies. In Belgium, with bugles sounding the charge and their colors flying, the 33rd French Infantry Regiment smashed head-on into the Germans, making an all-or-nothing charge. In it, Lieutenant Charles de Gaulle was wounded leading his platoon. In the Second World War he would become the leader of the Free French and, later, President of France.

The rosy picture of the war darkened suddenly for the Kaiser and his generals. In the east, the Russian Bear awoke. Russian armies appeared earlier than the Germans had anticipated. The hordes of Russians were ill-equipped, but they forced the Germans to fight in eastern Europe before they were ready.

Hard fighting on two fronts at the same time was not according to plan. General von Moltke began to lose his nerve. The secret plan called for fast action through Belgium, then the defeat of France, followed by the crushing of Russia. The Germans in France were behind their timetable. The resistance of the tiny Belgian Army had upset it.

Von Moltke had a custom which caused him trouble. He stayed far behind the German armies, out of touch with the sit-

uation. This was before the day of effective radio. The field
telephone of 1914 was not equal to the situation, and events
changed too quickly for telegraph wires to be laid between key
points. Field Marshal von Moltke was groping in a maze caused
by lack of information. He was neither a driver nor a general
who could inspire his men.

The German general also lacked confidence in himself. Instead of holding in the Alsace-Lorraine region, he changed the
scheme and attacked. This attack was defeated. And, worse, he
weakened his right wing by taking 85,000 soldiers from it, sending them to Russia. The general who had conceived the plan
nine years before, Count von Schlieffen, must have whirled in
his grave.

The French, finally alerted by news of the tremendous advance through Belgium and its threat, worked hard to meet it.
This was not easy, because they had to rearrange their armies
to try to stop the mass of Germans.

Tourists were trying frantically to rush out of France. They
clogged the English Channel ports. They paid sky-high prices
for meals and lodging. They wanted to get home, and it seemed
almost impossible.

King George V and the Prince of Wales, wearing military
uniforms, appeared with the Queen on a balcony at Buckingham
Palace to receive the cheers of the crowd.

Prices in Britain zoomed. The faces of the people showed
everything from despair to enthusiasm. To some, the war meant
adventure. Reservists carrying kit bags jammed the railroad stations on the way to their units in the British Expeditionary
Force. The English looked for a short war, but their Secretary
of State for War, Lord Kitchener, startled them by saying that
the war would last three years, maybe longer, and that a large
army would be needed.

The British Expeditionary Force (BEF) drew ball ammuni-
tion and emergency rations, and said good-by. It entrained for
Channel ports. Its leader was an old soldier, Field Marshal Sir
John French. He had courage but was easily irritated. He seemed

to belong to the previous century. Haig, one of his generals, wrote in his diary, "I know in my heart Sir John French is not fit to command." Sir John's BEF consisted of about 125,000 regulars. "A contemptible little army," the Kaiser called it. Troubles lay ahead for the BEF, but in the Battle of the Marne, when the freedom of France was at stake, it played a notable role.

Chapter 4

THE WRECK OF THE WHEEL

THE over-all commander of the French Army was an officer
who looked like a tired old fullback, General Joseph Joffre.
He was a bulky fellow with a stomach so large his black uniform
could not conceal it. His red breeches bagged at the knees.

"*Mes enfants*"—"my children"—he called his soldiers, and
they nicknamed him "Papa" Joffre. He was not a dynamic, brilliant leader, but no soldier in any army had more courage. While
the soldiers regarded Joffre as an affectionate papa, his generals
took a different view. Although General Joffre was placid about
events, he could become angry at individuals. He looked like a
friendly grandfather, but he was a hard, demanding leader. He
was a difficult man for his generals to work for because he permitted no mistakes. One error and the senior officer was out of
a job. His staff officers were not placid people, for General
Joffre had a habit of keeping his own counsel.

When Joffre first heard from one of his generals, General
Charles Lanrézac, that the Germans were streaming through
Belgium and were entering France from the north, he was unconcerned. Old Papa Joffre jammed his red and gold cap on his
white hair all the tighter. He was not anxious to hear about the
Belgian border. He wanted to hear about his armies fighting in
Alsace-Lorraine. He felt it was a point of honor to win back the
"lost provinces." After Joffre received word of the Germans in
the north, eight days passed before he sent an army north. It
was commanded by Lanrézac.

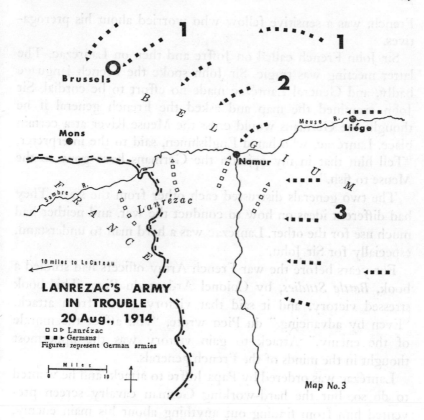

**LANREZAC'S ARMY
IN TROUBLE
20 Aug., 1914**

□ □ ▷ Lanrézac
■ ■ ▶ Germans
Figures represent German armies

Miles
0   10

Map No. 3

General Lanrézac was an odd individual. He had trouble controlling his temper. He was well-educated, but was burdened with a sour disposition and he criticized everyone freely. This, and his rudeness, eventually led to his downfall.

When Lanrézac's army marched north it soon found itself in a desperate situation.

There was help not far away, for the British Expeditionary Force was landing in France and was en route to Le Cateau. The "Old Contemptibles," as the British soldiers called themselves, were riding in trucks marked "*Hommes*—40; *Chevaux*—8" —forty men or eight horses. The British general, Sir John

French, was a sensitive fellow who worried about his preroga-
tives.

Sir John French called on Joffre and then on Lanrézac. The
latter meeting was tragic. Sir John spoke the French language
badly, and General Lanrézac made no effort to be cordial. Sir
John examined the map and asked the French general if he
thought the Germans would cross the Meuse River at a certain
place. Lanrézac, who hated Englishmen, said to the interpreter,
"Tell him that in my opinion the Germans have gone to the
Meuse to fish."

The two generals distrusted each other from the start. They
had different ideas on how to conduct the war, and neither had
much use for the other. Lanrézac was a hard man to understand,
especially for Sir John.

For years before the war French Army officers had studied a
book, *Battle Studies*, by Colonel Ardant du Picq. This book
stressed victory, and it said that victory comes from attack.
"Even by advancing," du Picq wrote, "you affect the morale
of the enemy." Attack to gain victory was the uppermost
thought in the minds of the French generals.

Lanrézac was ordered by Papa Joffre to attack, and he wanted
to do so, but the hard-working German cavalry screen prevented him from finding out anything about his main enemy,
the German infantry. When Lanrézac finally saw that his army
was outnumbered he withdrew, and this was a hard thing for
him to do.

Shortly a nine-mile gap developed between the BEF, in line
of battle at Mons, and General Lanrézac's army. This gap was
serious, for, if the Germans discovered it, they could pour
through unhindered and could strike both armies in the flank
and rear. The little British Expeditionary Force particularly was
in danger. It not only had a nine-mile gap on its right, but in
front of it was a tremendous German force.

Not only were the English outnumbered, but they were up
against crack German troops. Hard, realistic peacetime training

had made the German Army difficult to beat, and it saved German lives.

The German privates themselves were efficient. For example, before the Germans and the British clashed, Private August Assel, slender, trim-looking scout of the 4th Squadron Heavy Cavalry, walked ahead of his squadron. He had his rifle loaded, at the ready. It was the heavy cavalry's job to bull its way through any opposition. This did not mean it would blunder into enemy guns.

August Assel walked carefully. He knew that sooner or later his squadron would strike the enemy. Because of fog and uncertainty, the major of the heavy cavalry had ordered that the horses be left behind. His troopers were spread across the fields in infantry advance formation.

When Private Assel reached the crest of a hill, the fog lifted. He climbed a haystack to get a better look. Across a little valley were soldiers digging a trench. His field glasses told him they were British. He drew a sketch. On it, he marked the places where powerful guns were being placed. Then he estimated distances from the haystack to parts of the enemy trench and jotted them on his drawing. Next, he took a comfortable, prone position, aimed his rifle, and sent forty rounds whistling across the valley. The British stopped work and jumped in their trench. They tried to locate the enemy. The rapid fire made them think they were attacked by numbers of men.

When British rifle fire plunked into his haystack, Assel slid down and ran back over the hill to his major. "Here is a sketch of the British position," he said.

August Assel's drawing saved his regiment lives and time. The heavy cavalry regiment moved quickly into a good position and outfought the British. When General Ludendorff heard about Private Assel's work, he ordered that the young soldier receive the Iron Cross, First Class.

The British pulled back. Retreating dulls morale, but the British were not downhearted when they took position along a little canal near the small town of Mons. Thousands and thousands of shells rained on the Englishmen, but they did not quit. The Germans in their gray uniforms attacked in mass. A hard battle got under way. The Germans decimated the British units, which in turn riddled them with accurate rifle fire.

While the generals on both sides groped for information about each other's forces, the soldiers were under an even greater strain. The Germans were tired from their long march and fight through Belgium, and the men of the BEF now realized they were outnumbered.

At Mons, "L" Battery of the Royal Horse Artillery fired its guns until all but one of them were knocked out, and then until that one was out of ammunition. Four brave men stayed at that cannon and served it, even though the Germans were only a short distance away. All the other men of "L" Battery were killed or wounded.

The Germans seemed to be everywhere. The French general, Lanrézac, who was hard pressed, saw that he had to withdraw his army or lose it. Sir John French, on hearing that the French were pulling back, retreated with his army. The co-operation between the rude, English-hating Lanrézac and the sensitive Sir John became worse as the retreat went on.

The retreat of the French and British was hard. There was no rest. The August-September days were scorchers. Wretched refugees with their children thronged the roads. They made travel impossible.

Both sides lost heavily. One leader did not show that he was worried: Papa Joffre. His calmness buoyed up those about him. In Paris there was great excitement. The streets were barricaded. The Parisians wanted no Germans, for they had had their fill in the War of 1870.

Urged on by Joffre, Lanrézac was able to halt and counterattack. He did not win, but stopping the retreat for even a short time improved the morale of his soldiers.

In America, newspapers featured the war news. It appeared

as though the Germans were conquering France. People felt a friendly sentiment toward France because the Marquis de Lafayette helped George Washington's Continental Army; others looked upon England as the mother country. Although large numbers of Americans favored the Germans, most Americans wanted the Allies to win.

The German "wheel" rolled on. On September 2, 1914, the hard-pressed BEF stood twenty miles from Paris. France seemed doomed. Papa Joffre did two important things. He drew a line across the map south of Paris along the Seine River and said there would be no retreat beyond that line. Then he formed a new army, which he placed on the left of the BEF.

During the fighting around Paris, two French regiments, about 6,000 men, were hauled to the front in taxis. Later on, this incident grew into the legend that "the taxi cabs saved Paris." This is probably the first time that numbers of motor vehicles were used in war.

The enemy was having its troubles—it always does. Field Marshal von Moltke, worried because he had sent troops to fight the Russians, decided that his soldiers were covering too wide a front. He pulled his First Army east of Paris. This was the army, the tip of the scythe, that was supposed to drive west of Paris and cut it off from the rest of France.

Once more the secret plan of Count von Schlieffen was weakened by von Moltke. The map on page 34 shows how von Moltke altered the plan.

The outlook for France and the British Expeditionary Force was dark. French political leaders visited General Joffre to try to discover how he was going to stop the Germans. Papa Joffre had plans to strike at the Germans, depending on whether they advanced to the east or the west of Paris, but he did not tell anyone.

One of Joffre's greatest problems was not the enemy or the politicians, but the irritable attitude of the British leader in France, Sir John French. A telegram from Sir John stating that

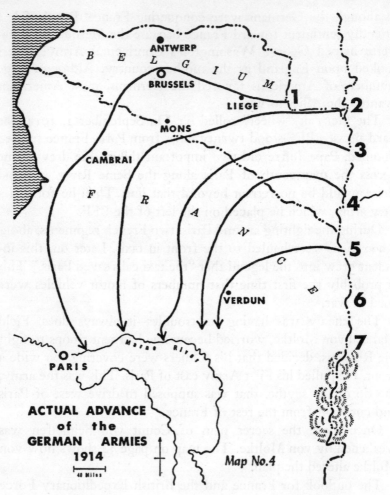

ACTUAL ADVANCE
of the
GERMAN ARMIES
1914

Map No.4

the British Army was tired and was going to take a ten-day rest, that they could not fill a gap in the line, made Papa Joffre raise his bushy white eyebrows. When news of Sir John's attitude reached England, Lord Kitchener made a trip to France to investigate. When he appeared he wore his Field Marshal's uniform, and this upset the thin-skinned Sir John French.

General French was a man to whom trifles seemed big. He

felt that Lord Kitchener should have worn civilian clothing—
that Kitchener's putting on his uniform was a sign that he wanted
everyone to know that he outranked Sir John. Lord Kitchener
was not worrying about rank. He wanted to get the job done.

The meeting between the two generals took place in the British Embassy in Paris. Kitchener listened to Sir John a few moments, then took him into a private room. No one is sure exactly
what else took place between the two Englishmen, but after
Lord Kitchener left Sir John started to co-operate with General
Joffre.

Shortly after this meeting, and before he gave out his long-
looked-for attack order, Papa Joffre studied each of his generals.
He wanted each one to be imbued with the will to attack and
win. Only in this way could lower-ranking officers, noncommissioned officers, and privates be inspired. Papa Joffre knew
that Lanrézac was brilliant, but he saw that he was now tired
and hesitant. Lanrézac's bitter criticisms were doing damage.
The French commander in chief realized that Sir John found
it hard to co-operate with so rude an officer, so Joffre relieved
Lanrézac and gave his job to another French general.

Sir John French felt better, but his mood was not one of happiness; it was an anxious time. The fate of France and England
was on the scales.

On the fourth of September, Joffre decided he could trap
the enemy. Secretly, he transferred troops from Lorraine westward to Paris. The Germans, sweeping south, were east of Paris.
Joffre's new army lashed out and hit the nearest German army
in the flank. The fight along the Marne River was fierce. It was
one of the most important battles in the world's history.

At a crucial time in the battle, Joffre became ill. The old
leader sent an Order of the Day from his hospital bed:

AT THIS MOMENT WE ARE ENGAGED IN THE BATTLE
ON WHICH DEPENDS THE FUTURE OF OUR COUNTRY.
. . . NO ONE MUST LOOK BACK. TROOPS THAT CANNOT
ADVANCE MUST HOLD THEIR GROUND.

At this crisis, General von Moltke was 160 miles away from his right flank, the most important army in the German plan. He could not make his leadership felt.

Von Moltke was in trouble, for a gap developed between his First and Second armies. Instead of taking an automobile top-speed for the battle area, or at least sending his best and most senior staff officer, von Moltke sent Lieutenant Colonel Richard Hentsch. Hentsch had had little experience.

When Colonel Hentsch arrived at the Second German Army, he found that its commander, frightened because the BEF was advancing into a gap, had ordered a retreat. Colonel Hentsch approved. When Hentsch saw another gap, he ordered the First German Army to retreat. So two German armies were thrown into retreat by the inexperienced staff officer.

Many German soldiers in ranks were amazed. In most of the armies they were winning, and they had been winning since early August. They could not understand why they were being ordered back.

Von Moltke was greatly excited. He reported to the Kaiser, "Your Majesty, we have lost the war." The Kaiser did not think so, but he had had enough of Count von Moltke, so he relieved him of his command.

In honor of the timely victory at the Marne River, General Joffre published another Order of the Day, telling of the defeat of the first four German armies. He told how numerous wounded had been left behind by the enemy, and about the great numbers of prisoners and munitions that had been captured. He thanked his officers, noncommissioned officers and men. Joffre was the hero of the hour.

The Kaiser's new senior general in France was the severe and strong-minded General Erich von Falkenhayn.

A "race to the sea" developed in which both sides tried to get around the other's flank. A stirring incident happened near Nieuport, Belgium. French Zouaves were guarding a bridge on the Yser Canal. Early morning mists boiled up from the water.

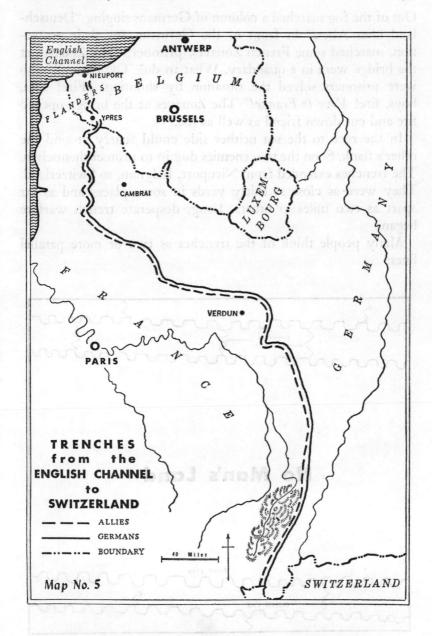

English
Channel

ANTWERP

NIEUPORT

B E L G I U M

F L A N D E R S

YPRES

BRUSSELS

CAMBRAI

LUXEM-
BOURG

F R A N C E

VERDUN

PARIS

G E R M A N Y

**TRENCHES
from   the
ENGLISH CHANNEL
to
SWITZERLAND**

– – – – –   ALLIES
————   GERMANS
—·—·—·—   BOUNDARY

40 Miles

SWITZERLAND

Map No. 5

Out of the fog marched a column of Germans singing "Deutschland über Alles." In front of the Germans, for their protection, marched some French Zouaves, prisoners. The Zouaves at the bridge were in a quandary. What to do? The Zouaves who were prisoners solved the situation by shouting, "Fire! Fire, boys, fire! *Vive la France!*" The Zouaves at the bridge opened fire and cut down friend as well as foe.

In the race to the sea neither side could scurry around the other's flank. Soon the two enemies dug in to protect themselves. The trenches extended from Nieuport, Belgium, to Switzerland. They were as close as thirty yards in some places and as far apart as two miles in others. Long, desperate trench warfare began.

Many people think of the trenches as two or more parallel lines:

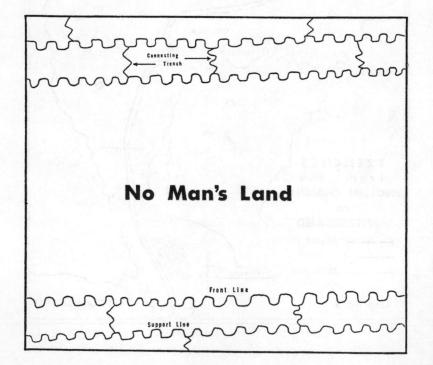

Actually, as the war went on, the trenches formed a maze.

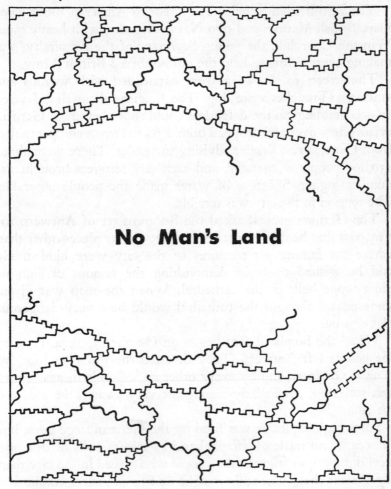

No Man's Land

The situation near the northern end of the line, in Antwerp, was serious for the Allies. Here the German army under General von Beseler was besieging King Albert's army and the city. When von Beseler brought up siege artillery and pounded the concrete forts about the city into rubble, he doomed Antwerp. The situation in the besieged town was worsened by a shortage of water and by the arrival of crowds of homeless farmers and people from the outer villages. Every day more refugees came.

The British tried to help. They sent to Antwerp about 8,000 men, British Marines and two Naval Brigades, with heavy guns. Winston Churchill, the young Secretary of the Admiralty, was making every effort to help the outnumbered British Army.

The streets of Antwerp were barricaded with wagons and sandbags. Trenches were dug. The Belgians themselves leveled 10,000 buildings so the defenders could shoot better. A German aviator flew over and dropped bombs on the town and pamphlets from General von Beseler advising surrender. There were about 450,000 people in the city, and each day refugees brought the number higher. Shortage of water made the people miserable. The tension in the city was terrible.

The German general asked the Burgomaster of Antwerp for a map so that he could have his artillery fire at places other than where the famous art treasures of the city were hidden. He said he wished to avoid demolishing the famous carillon of ninety-nine bells in the cathedral. When the map was given, some people thought the cathedral would be a very dangerous place to be.

When the bombardment began on October 7, 1914, most of the people left Antwerp. They deserted the town on foot, by boat, by dogcart, and by every other conceivable means. There was suffering, particularly among the very young, the old, and the sick.

Some high explosive was fired by the German siege guns, but the crack and rattle of shrapnel and its rain of balls of iron and steel did more to frighten the people who stayed in the city than the heavier shells. Oil tanks caught on fire and black smoke and red flames shot into the air. The defending troops pulled out, and October 9 the Burgomaster surrendered the town.

King Albert and his army escaped to fight for the Allies in Flanders.

The First World War had been under way since August. Much damage had been done, but even more frightful times lay ahead.

Chapter 5

RUSSIA AGAINST GERMANY;
BATTLE OF TANNENBERG

WHILE the German wheel was grinding through Belgium and France, the Russian Army was getting ready to fight. Russia, with a population of 170,000,000 and an army of 15,000,000, looked like a steam roller, but she was not. The feeling existed over the world that Russia had unlimited and tremendous military strength. This was a myth. However, the Russians did get ready to fight faster than the Germans expected.

When the Czar of Russia, Nicholas II, signed the order sending his country to war, his subjects were enthusiastic. Crowds appeared in front of the British, French, and Serbian embassies in the capital, St. Petersburg—later called Leningrad—and cheered.

But Russia had a big count against her before any one of her soldiers sighted the enemy: she lacked the industry necessary to win in modern war. Where countries like Great Britain had one hundred and fifty factories, Russia had one. Considering that the Russian countryside seemed to stretch forever, she had few miles of railroad track, and this proved a handicap when she faced the task of moving her huge armies and supplying them. The Russian Bear did not know how to develop potential military might. He looked ready to grip his enemies in a bear hug and crush them, but this was a false picture.

Precious little money had been spent on the Russian Army since it suffered defeat by the Japanese nine years before the

First World War. And the money spent did not always produce results, because of graft. The Russian Army had few trucks, motor cars, and airplanes. It was rushing to war deficient in artillery, "the infantryman's best friend." Germany had ten times as many heavy cannons as Russia. There was also a shortage of artillery shells for the Russian artillery.

In Wild West shows, popular in that day in the United States, one of the most enjoyable acts was the appearance of the Russian Cossacks. These expert riders were billed as "the wild horsemen of the steppes"—the plains. The word "Cossack" frightened people, but it was another myth, for the Russian cavalry was inefficient, and the larger the group the more poorly it performed.

Noncommissioned officers are the backbone of any army. They are the leaders who are closest to the privates, and they are necessarily in great number. Russia had trouble finding non-commissioned officers, because of the lack of education of the Russian people. Great numbers of their N.C.O.'s were ignorant and illiterate. Regardless of other things about their army, this spelled failure.

There were also few technical experts in the army of the Czar. The lack of training in radio and in coding and decoding of messages would prove costly.

The Russian colonels and many other high officers were lazy. There were no new ideas in the army since its defeat by Japan. The Russian War Minister, Sukhomlinov, set the example in lack of thirst for knowledge when he boasted, "I have not read a military manual in twenty-five years."

But the Russian soldiers could withstand hardship. Approximately two-thirds of the Czar's army was composed of native Russians, one-third of conquered peoples such as the Poles. Most of the privates had been peasants. They were used to receiving orders, they had a childlike faith in their leaders, and their happy-go-lucky natures carried them a long way in such a poor organization. Their hardiness made them soldiers who could not be discounted. They could sleep on the ground in the uniforms they had worn all day, rise in the morning, eat scanty breakfasts, march as long as they were ordered to, with no complaints. They were ready to die trying. However, too often, the Russian Army lacked the vital *esprit de corps* of the German units— the spirit of the unit, which binds a well-trained military organization together and helps it to gain victory in darkness and in times of stress.

The war between Germany and Russia was influenced by the vastness of Russia. The country seemed endless. Any army entering it must worry about being struck from an unexpected angle, about being cut off from supplies.

When the Russians began to fight, they spread out, because of the odd geographical position of Poland, then part of the Czar's territory.

A ray of hope was nursed in German headquarters. Maybe the five armies of the Czar could be cut off.

But the Grand Duke, commanding for the Czar, himself saw the danger. He spread out his armies and decided to attack as soon as possible. The target was East Prussia, the home of the German ruling class.

Plans can look fine on paper. But on the ground the soldiers must contend with the weather, rivers, hills, swamps, and hardships. The first obstacle in the Grand Duke's way was the fifty-mile stretch of Masurian Lakes. The Germans had armed steamboats on them.

The Grand Duke dreamed of striking into East Prussia. It would be great to ravage the rich homes of the hated German generals and political leaders. He sent one army, under General Rennenkampf, north of the lakes. The other army, marching up from the south, was commanded by General Samsonov. These were two old soldiers. But more than the chain of lakes prevented the two Russians from helping each other. They hated one another. They were deadly personal enemies.

Long ago when they were young, on a campaign against the Japanese in Manchuria, China, the two Russians had fought one

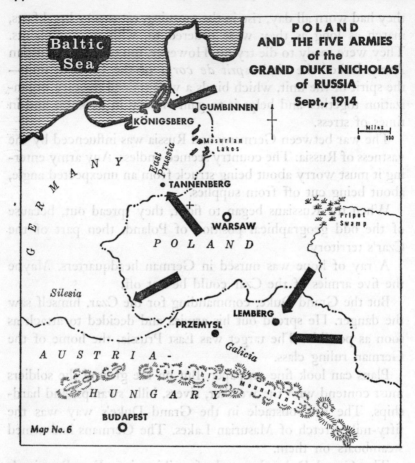

POLAND
AND THE FIVE ARMIES
of the
GRAND DUKE NICHOLAS
of RUSSIA
Sept., 1914

Baltic Sea

GUMBINNEN
KÖNIGSBERG
Masurian Lakes
East Prussia
GERMANY
TANNENBERG
WARSAW
Pripet Swamp
P O L A N D
Silesia
LEMBERG
PRZEMYSL
Galicia
A U S T R I A -
Carpathian Mountains
H U N G A R Y
BUDAPEST

Map No. 6

Miles
0   100

another with their fists on a railway platform. General Rennen-kampf was an odd-looking individual with a handlebar mustache sticking out six inches from his cheeks. Samsonov wore a beard. He was fat, but he had a good mind; he was loved by his troops. Both were supposed to be great leaders.

The German General Max von Prittwitz, a nervous, uncertain officer, knew the Russian plans, not only because of daring spies, but because the Russian radio messages were sent in the clear rather than in code. Von Prittwitz decided to defeat the northern Russian army first. But von Prittwitz did not know that one of his subordinate generals, the headstrong Hermann von François, had already attacked.

François saw streams of refugees heading back from the border, trying to get away from the Russians. To General François the soil of East Prussia was "sacred." He plunged into the northern army of Russians with all the men he could muster. His attack caused the Russians to lose several thousand in killed, wounded, and missing, but General François' victory was a hollow one, for it looked as though his superior, von Prittwitz, would now have to advance farther to the east in order to defeat the Russians. Von Prittwitz worried. If he attacked eastward the Russians coming from the south could strike him in the back.

Now the German General von Mackensen, a corps commander, decided to attack like François. Mackensen, a white-haired, white-mustached, tough character, was near the town of Gumbinnen. At night, things went wrong. His German soldiers received confusing orders. They fell into column to march, then waited a long time on the road. They advanced a few miles on the road, then received orders to turn around and march back. All night the tired Germans under von Mackensen milled about. The soldiers began to think their leaders did not know their own minds. The officers ordered an attack. Suddenly, the Russians counterattacked and the German soldiers ran.

Von Mackensen tried personally to stem the panic, and in doing so he lost control of his force. Other German officers tried to stop the rush of the Germans from the battlefield. Von Mackensen seized the German colors and spread them across his chest. He cried to the panic-ridden soldiers dashing by, "He who deserts his flag is yellow!" But soldiers streamed on past the black, red, and white flag.

When von Prittwitz heard news from Gumbinnen at his headquarters far away, he panicked, too. Without telling his staff, he got on the telephone and put in a call across Europe to von Moltke, in Luxembourg, Belgium. General von Prittwitz told of his troubles. He seemed not to know what to do, so von Moltke took his army away from him.

Two men were sent to the east to relieve von Prittwitz. The German General Paul von Hindenburg was called from retirement. As his principal helper he was given General Ludendorff. This was smart. Old von Hindenburg knew every foot of East Prussia. He was a general with moral courage. He could stay with a decision. He looked to the Germans as they thought a general ought to look. He had a bulky frame, a heavy, stern-looking face. Some thought he looked like the ancient German god, Wotan.

Hindenburg's chief of staff, Ludendorff, had physical courage. It was he who knocked on the gates of the fortress at Liége and demanded its surrender. He was a student of modern war and a capable staff general. The team Hindenburg-Ludendorff worked so well, and each part of the team was so dependent on the other, that Winston Churchill, writing about them after the war, used the symbol HL to denote their efficient and close work.

When Hindenburg and Ludendorff arrived at General von Prittwitz' headquarters, they found the situation better than they had expected. The two Germans benefited from the advice of a keen staff officer, Lieutenant Colonel Carl Hoffmann. Hoffmann adjusted his monocle and showed HL the map. He pointed out in terse terms how victory could be won. Hindenburg approved the daring plan, and Ludendorff worked it out.

The Germans pulled their forces away from the front of the northern Russian army and brought them south to strike in the rear of the southern Russian army, marked + on the map.

Poor Samsonov, in command at Tannenberg, was handicapped by inadequate railroads. He could not move fast.

The northern Russian army helped its enemy because its commander, General Rennenkampf, did not move his army for sixty hours. He did not know where the Germans in front of him had gone, and he sent no cavalry to find out. He was lulled to sleep by the battle of Gumbinnen, which he chose to consider a victory. Also, he sent radio messages, in the clear rather than in secret code, telling that he was going to march straight west to capture the German fortress Königsberg, on the Baltic Sea. Poor radio work by the Russians let the German generals know what the Russians planned to do.

General Hindenburg's smashing victory at Tannenberg made him into a national hero. It eased the disappointment over the failure of the Germans to defeat France.

The team of Hindenburg and Ludendorff then swept the German armies northeast into the lake country, where they defeated the Russian Rennenkampf. The German General François sent his men through a gap in the wild lake country. They struck the Russians savagely in the flank and rear.

The Germans were fearless as they headed into Russia. In places they swept over the huge, feudal farms far behind the Russian lines, even capturing artillery. Aggressiveness by leaders in all grades helped the Germans. For instance, Sergeant Major Gustav Pitschel commanded a platoon of twenty-four soldiers. They were marching over the endless fields, guarding a flank of their regiment.

A Russian peasant, carrying a sack of beets, plodded across a field toward the platoon. Gustav stopped him and said "Hey, Ivan, tell us where our enemies are?"

The peasant lowered his sack and pointed. The words tumbled. "In that forest, Mister General, is a camp of the Czar's soldiers. They robbed me, stole my pigs."

"So?" said the sergeant major. "How many?"

"Two," the peasant said.

"A camp of two soldiers?"

"No, no! Two pigs." The peasant laughed and said slowly, "They—take—two—pigs—mine—robbers."

"But how many soldiers?" Gustav Pitschel pressed.

The peasant flashed his finger so many times that Pitschel lost count. He estimated the peasant meant five hundred. Gustav Pitschel studied the woods a mile away through his field glasses. He thought he saw smoke filtering up through the woods. He wet his lips. Perhaps that was the enemy's camp.

Gustav thanked the peasant and ordered his men to follow.

Shortly, the twenty-four Germans were in position on the ridge looking down into the Russian camp.

The Russian soldiers, maybe four hundred, were cooking breakfast. A few were chopping wood. The echo of the axes biting into the fallen trees sounded on the ridge as if a giant were knocking on a door. Along the edge of the forest fresh dirt outlined a trench. Five horses were tied to a picket line at the back of the camp.

If young Sergeant Major Pitschel was nervous he did not show it. He tugged at the black beard covering his face. Gus liked that beard, for it made him look older. *Can twenty-four men attack four hundred?* he mused.

Gustav Pitschel made his platoon lie flat along the ridge.

The Russians below were unaware of the danger. A cook at a campfire shouted, and a line formed for breakfast. A few Russians hung out washing on the branches of trees.

"Two hundred meters," Gustav said quietly to his platoon. "When I give the order, rapid fire. Aim low." While his infantrymen readied themselves and picked their targets, Sergeant Major Pitschel wrote out a message and sent it by runner back across the fields to his colonel.

At Gustav's signal, the twenty-four Germans opened fire. The roar of the volley sounded like Hell had broken loose. The Russians were completely surprised. Two of them fell dead into a campfire. Six were wounded. Some sprinted for the trench and hid. Others sought their weapons and started to fire wildly at the ridge. The camp was in confusion. The Russian officers were unequal to the situation.

Gustav Pitschel now ordered half of his men to fire while he and the remaining men sprinted for the Russian camp. "Surrender!" Gustav shouted. Three hundred and forty panic-stricken Russians held up their hands. Gustav was delirious with excitement. He beckoned with his arm and his twelve men back on the ridge stopped firing and ran to him.

Suddenly a Russian captain shouted, "A disgrace! They are only a handful. Let us fight!"

In the wild, hand-to-hand battle, men fired their weapons without aim. One Russian fell wounded, knocking over a pot of gruel suspended over a fire and scalding himself. Five horses belonging to Russian officers stampeded. Two Germans fell dead near Gustav. Three more were wounded. With his pistol blazing in one hand, his sword in the other slashing at Russians, the screaming Gustav Pitschel looked like an ancient German god.

In a moment, it looked as though Gustav's surprise attack would fail. Another German was shot down. But Pitschel's message to his colonel saved him. When the colonel received the message he double-timed his regiment toward the fight. When the Russians saw the regiment they ran from the wood, leaving twelve dead and many wounded. Fifty-five others stood with their hands up. Later, when his general heard of Gustav's exploit, he pinned the Iron Cross, First Class, to the sergeant major's coat.

The Germans were well-trained, but this did not solve the problem of the wide waste land. However, there was a key: the Russian armies were spread far apart. When they were beaten they retreated in disorder. In less than a month they had lost 310,000 men and 500 cannons. Among their casualties were many noncommissioned officers, something Russia could not afford.

After a battle at the Masurian Lakes a German officer congratulated General von Hindenburg. The ponderous old general nodded his head. "Thank you," he said. "But remember this— there is another man on this battlefield who feels as low as I am happy—the Russian commander."

The defeats at the battle of Tannenberg and at the Masurian Lakes helped bring on grave days in the interior of Russia. They were days which would have an effect on the world for a period longer than any man could foresee.

Chapter 6

AUSTRIA TRIES TO PUNISH SERBIA

THE Germans rolling through France received great publicity. The names of the places were more or less familiar to the English-speaking world, and in France it was easy for war correspondents to file their dispatches. Consequently, much more was published about the Western Front than the war in the east. In the Galician country, in Russia, in Serbia, and in other Balkan countries, the names were jawbreakers to western peoples.[1] There were few correspondents with the armies in the east. As a result, little became known about the bloody eastern campaigns.

Not only were place names new to newspaper readers, but the battle leader who would guide the Austrians through most of the war was practically unknown. He was an odd character, Conrad von Hotzendorff, the son of an Austrian cavalry colonel.

When Conrad was a boy, he studied hard, and consequently spoke eight languages. This enabled him to travel easily through large areas in Turkey, Russia, and into the mountainous country of Serbia before war broke, disguised as a peasant. Conrad became a dangerous, powerful man—part general, part politician. He believed that Austria could not survive surrounded by warlike people unless she herself were even more warlike. As field marshal, Conrad set the example in Spartan living for his soldiers by physical toil, and by working in winter in an office with no heat and the windows wide open. He was not a big man phys-

[1] See Map No. 1, page 15.

ically. He had alert eyes, a white mustache, and a frail body, but he was dynamic.

The first thing that Conrad and his Emperor, Francis Joseph, tried to do after war broke out was to punish Serbia. This was a real job, far more difficult than they realized.

Serbia was hated by Austria. Serbia was the place where the Austrian archduke was murdered—the spark that touched off the war.

Serbia had one of the toughest armies in Europe. It was only 200,000 strong, and it was short of machine guns and artillery. Its supply wagons were pulled by oxen. But the Serbs were spirited. They had confidence in their fighting abilities, for they had defeated the Turks and Bulgars just before the world war started. Serbia also had an unusual commander in chief, Field Marshal Putnik. He was a semi-invalid, but a real leader. Because of asthma he remained indoors, in a quiet, heated room, far from the fighting, but reports were rushed to him and he could tell his soldiers what to do. In Putnik's younger days he had learned the geography of his nation thoroughly, and so could remember where every stream and trail ran.

Conrad's Austrian columns, 480,000 strong, crossed two rivers and invaded the northwest corner of Serbia from two directions. The Serbian infantry scrambled up the steep mountains of the country like goats. They sent von Hotzendorff's armies back with losses. What was more important to Serbia, her soldiers captured rifles, ammunition, and other supplies they needed.

This success made the Serbs believe they could invade Austria, but smart strategy by von Hotzendorff made the Serbs pull back.

It appeared that the Austrians, coming again, would defeat the Serbs, but the rugged mountain people did not quit. Field Marshal Putnik said that his strategy was to "place the enemy in the Serbian national mud so as to hinder their movement and supplies." This was effective, and the Austrian soldiers suffered for lack of food.

When all seemed lost, King Peter of Serbia, a very old man but a last-ditch fighter, appeared before his soldiers and invited anyone with a faint heart to go home. He inspired his men. The Serbians clashed with their enemies in bitter November weather and cut through the Austrian center. The Austrians were beaten. So fast did the Serbs take them prisoner, it was hard to find guards to march them toward the rear. Long lines of Austrian soldiers, in their odd, flower-pot, parade-ground hats, were sent to the rear with only a few Serbs as guards. When the Serbs felt they could spare no more guards, they said to the prisoners, "Just follow the telegraph wires and you'll find the prison camp." It was strange to see unguarded prisoners marching to the rear.

Accounts varied as to the number of Austrians taken prisoner. The number was somewhere between 40,000 and 70,000. The Serbs also captured 192 cannons and 491 cartloads of ammunition. The Austrians were driven out of the tiny country in disgrace.

But the Serbian victory was crowned with torment, for typhus and cholera broke out. Serbia called for help, and doctors were sent from the United States, England, France, and Russia, but not before thousands died.

The little country did not breathe easily. They knew that if the Russians were beaten by the Germans they, in turn, would be smashed by the Kaiser's armies. The Serbs prayed for a Russian victory.

Chapter 7

ATTACK ON THE RUSSIAN BEAR

CONRAD VON HOTZENDORFF, of Austria, the baron who was supposed to have the intelligence of a genius, struck blindly at the Russians in southern Poland. He was heading into a trap, for the Russians had regrouped their armies.

Conrad had two serious counts against him. The Russians knew his plans, and he was forced to leave half of his army on the Serbian front.

Years before the war, the Russian Secret Service had discovered an Austrian colonel with poor morals. Rather than be exposed, the Austrian officer had given Conrad's secret plans to Russian spies. Knowing what Conrad planned to do was a big advantage to the Russians.

Conrad's Austrians plunged across the border into Russian Poland and were soon up against six Russian armies. At first they were successful, but the Russians engulfed the Austrians like a tidal wave and swept them back. The Austrian fortress at Lemberg fell. In the fierce fighting 350,000 Austrians lay dead or wounded on the field of battle, or were taken prisoner. It was slaughter, and, as always happens in a battle, many of the best leaders were killed. The Russians gained a stupendous victory in Galicia.

The retreat from the fortress at Lemberg was horrible. The Austrian soldiers and refugees crowded the roads, all mixed up. The rear guard action was scanty—anything but vigorous. Conrad's Austrians had one thought: to escape any Cossacks who

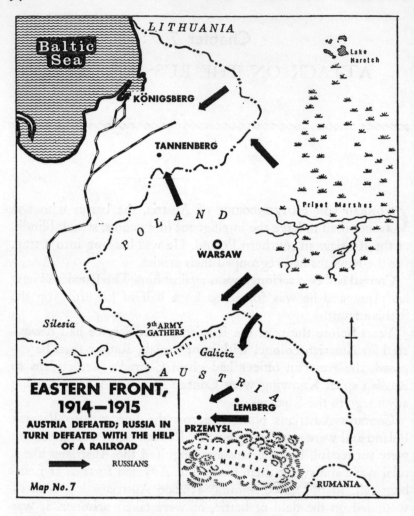

EASTERN FRONT,
1914–1915

AUSTRIA DEFEATED; RUSSIA IN
TURN DEFEATED WITH THE HELP
OF A RAILROAD

→ RUSSIANS

Map No. 7

might be riding after them. The retreat got out of hand and the Austrians withdrew 100 miles.

The Russians had an opportunity now. To the west lay the rich mineral districts of Silesia. Once the Russian Bear sank his claws into them he might never be pried loose.

In the south, the ancient fortress of Przemysl held, but a Russian force surrounded it and waited while other Russians pushed the Austrians into the Carpathian Mountains. The battles in Galicia wrecked most of Conrad's armies.

In the north, Hindenburg-Ludendorff, the HL combination, had an advantage on the Russians because of their efficient radio-intercept service. The radio messages of the Russian generals were still not in code and were easily translated by the Germans. In addition, the Russian armies moved slowly. To strike the Russian Bear in the south, Hindenburg-Ludendorff conceived a daring plan. They placed the German soldiers in the north on 750 railroad trains and moved them south. The Ninth German Army, as it was called, moved 475 miles to new battle grounds. Only an army having fine staff officers and an efficient railroad system at its disposal could accomplish such an unusual undertaking.

The appearance of the Germans near the southern tip of Silesia was a shock to the Russians pursuing Conrad. Here was Hindenburg-Ludendorff on their north flank ready to crush them. The Russians were surprised and dismayed.

Hindenburg's 9th Army struck toward the Vistula River.

The Russian armies were in grave peril, but they did not quit. To the contrary, the Russian generals tried to trap the Germans by swinging north behind Hindenburg's army. But the Russians spilled their plans on the radio and HL learned of the trap. They pulled back, leaving land mines behind them.

The Russians decided to march again into the valuable Silesian area. This was a four-army drive, but once again they told their plans on the radio.

The Germans knew that the Russians must be halted. Hindenburg and Ludendorff placed their army under the fighter von Mackensen, and put the soldiers back on the railroad trains. The army rolled north. The Austrians in the south marched up to take the place of the Germans as they moved north on the trains.

When General Mackensen had his army in position, he struck from the north against the Russian north flank. The Russians were badly surprised, but they reacted fast. They brought infantry up from the south in a grueling march, seventy miles in two days. In the battle it looked as if the Russians would take thousands of prisoners. They even sent to Warsaw for trains for the prisoners.

But a courageous German general, Scheffer, refused to quit. He and his three divisions, 60,000 men, hemmed in on all sides and outnumbered by the Russians, fought like maniacs. Scheffer inspired his troops. In a remarkable "ninth-inning" rally, Scheffer's attack not only saved the day, but captured 16,000 Russians. This battle made the Russian Bear forget about grabbing Silesia.

The longer the fighting lasted the worse conditions in the Czar's armies became. Many Russians were marching without rifles. Cannons were towed along by horses, but there was a lack of ammunition for them.

However, not everything was rosy for the Germans on the eastern front. The Kaiser was disappointed in the failure of his ally, Austria. The Austrian fortress Przemysl surrendered, and that dramatized the Austrian collapse. The soldiers in the fortress were starved. Their menu for two months was: breakfast, tea; dinner at noon, a small piece of meat with black bread; supper, tea and bread. And when the beef gave out the soldiers ate horse-meat. Dogs sold for ten dollars—and not as pets. As the cold winter days passed, the scanty rations were reduced. The Russians around the fort played a waiting game. They had plenty to eat and they knew of conditions inside. They preferred to capture the fortress by denying the garrison food. The Austrians taken prisoner at the surrender numbered about 100,000, and they faced days just as dismal in horrible Russian prison camps.

But the Russian fortunes elsewhere on the eastern front dwindled. They were gradually forced back all along the long battle line. Fighting in the winter was doubly hard on both sides. In February, 1915, alone, the Russians suffered 200,000 casualties.

The Germans pushed the Russian Bear back into the dreary Pripet marshes, one of the largest swamps in the world. The attack on East Prussia, Silesia, and Austria had cost Russia enormous casualties: 2,000,000 Russians had been killed, wounded, or were missing. The Czar of all the Russias decided to take active command of his armies. Because he was not trained or capable, this helped his enemies.

In the war in the west, as noted, the Kaiser had had all he could stomach of the vacillating general who had weakened the offensive through Belgium, von Moltke, so he replaced him with General Erich von Falkenhayn. The new commander in chief was alert, strong-minded, and arrogant. He was tall and erect, and his bristly haircut seemed to match his personality.

Von Falkenhayn was also smart. When Hindenburg-Ludendorff pressured him to have German soldiers shipped from France to the Russian front, and to have new units being formed in Germany accompany them, the new commander in chief of the German armies said, "No. The war will be won or lost in the West. Great Britain is the main enemy."

And events proved him right, until the United States entered the war on the side of the Allies.

Chapter 8

WARSHIPS AT THE DARDANELLES

THIS is the story of one of the most famous campaigns in history, and one of the saddest.

There was bungled planning in the Gallipoli campaign and lack of leadership by the British generals who commanded the soldiers. The airplane, the submarine, the machine gun, and the automatic rifle were new. Had they been misused there would have been an excuse, but planning and leadership were not new. Poor planning in London, and lack of leadership on the battlefield, brought humiliating defeat.

Before war broke, the British knew that the Germans were trying to make allies of the Turks. The German General Liman von Sanders, in 1913, brought a group of German officers to Constantinople and worked hard to improve the Turkish Army. The "Young Turks," the political party in power, appreciated this, and their ruthless leader, Enver Pasha, made a secret agreement with Germany.

Not everyone in Turkey was convinced that the Germans would make the best allies, but the British made a decision which the Young Turks used to turn public opinion against the British. The British were under contract to build two battleships for Turkey. The warships were being paid for by the Turkish people, by subscriptions and by contributions. All Turks were interested in the battleships. But the ships worried Britain. Winston Churchill, the young First Lord of the Admiralty, and his friend, Lord Fisher, his senior admiral, feared Turkey might enter the war on the side of the Germans. If this happened the two warships would be used against the Allies. It was a puzzling situation for the British Admiralty. The British broke the contract and kept the battleships.

People in Turkey were disappointed. The Young Turks used this incident to inflame the populace. General Liman von Sanders was quick. He arranged for his country to sell two warships to Turkey, and Turkey took a step closer to war on the side of the Germans.

But the Turks had serious worries. It was hard for them to know what to do. The Germans had failed to conquer France. In Galicia the Austrians had been beaten. And Germans living in the Turkish capital of Constantinople (now Istanbul) took pains to say that, if the Allies won, the ancient enemy of the Turks, the Russians, would be more powerful than ever. So Turkey jumped into the war by having her fleet bombard the Russian seaport of Odessa at the northern part of the Black Sea.

The Dardanelles was closed. This was a calamity for Russia, because she depended on France and England for ammunition, and the only good supply route lay through the Dardanelles.

The rash political general of Turkey, Enver Pasha, now attacked. The pompous, heel-clicking little officer believed that a victorious campaign against the Russians in winter would make everyone recognize him as one of the world's greatest generals. He refused advice. It was January, but he led 90,000 Turkish soldiers into the wild Caucasus Mountains at the eastern end of the Black Sea. The result was incredible. Eighty-one thousand Turks were killed in battle, or starved, or were frozen to death.

Russia feared more attacks and pleaded for help. As a result, the most forceful man in England, Lord Kitchener, assembled the British War Council to consider the proposed plan of sending the fleet through the Dardanelles, slicing Turkey in two, and reopening the supply line to Russia. Kitchener did not like the idea. He believed every available soldier should fight in France. But he listened to Winston Churchill.

Churchill was on fire with the idea of forcing the Dardanelles,

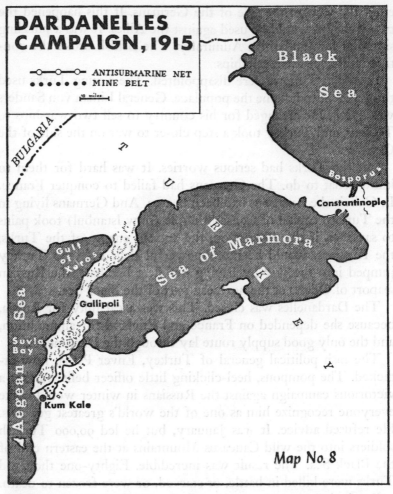

DARDANELLES
CAMPAIGN, 1915

○—○—○ ANTISUBMARINE NET
••••••• MINE BELT

10 miles

BULGARIA

Black
Sea

Bosporus

Constantinople

Sea of Marmora

Gulf
of
Xeros

Gallipoli

Suvla
Bay

Aegean Sea

Kum Kale

Map No. 8

and the more he talked, with his marvelous command of the English language, the more entranced the War Council became. The idea of sending the British fleet to the Dardanelles waters seemed smart to everyone but Kitchener. However, he finally gave in. The council session ended with the order that the fleet would bombard and "take" the Gallipoli peninsula. How a fleet was to take a peninsula was not explained. The campaign started on this vague note.

Winston Churchill believed the fleet could sweep the mines in the Dardanelles, knock out Turkish forces guarding the straits by gunfire, and sail on into the Black Sea. His friend, Admiral Lord Fisher, was not so sure.

A British fleet of twelve battleships, accompanied by four French battleships, sailed on the mission. One of the ships was the *Queen Elizabeth*, the most powerful war vessel afloat. She had eight powerful guns with bores fifteen inches wide, about sixteen six-inch guns, and many others of smaller caliber. The date was January, 1915.

In the Dardanelles, the Turks had planted eleven mine fields and an antisubmarine net. The mines, iron balls four feet in diameter and crammed with high-explosive, were anchored out of sight beneath the surface of the water. They were arranged with fuses which, if bumped by a ship, would cause the mine to explode, tearing the bottom out of the vessel.

British trawlers, working in pairs and equipped with cables and underwater kites, sailed into the Dardanelles. The flat-bottomed boats swept up some of the mines, and the dreadnaughts steamed on in. The farther into the straits the warships sailed, the hotter became the fire from the Turkish batteries on shore. Mobile Turkish field artillery dashed up, unlimbered their guns, and opened fire.

It was hard to sweep mines under fire. Vice Admiral Sackville Carden, the British leader, ordered his ships to pull back where they would be safe. After two more tries, Admiral Carden became ill and returned to England.

His place was taken by a rugged-looking seadog, Admiral John de Robeck, who was not as forceful as his appearance. After a nine-day wait, which enabled the Turks to make repairs to their forts, de Robeck attacked again with his fleet. The battleships thundered at the Turkish forts on both sides of the straits. But not all the mines had been swept up. Five battleships struck mines, and two of the ships sank, carrying more than two thousand men with them. Admiral de Robeck knew that a current flowed through the Dardanelles, and he thought his warships were striking floating mines placed in the water by the Turks. The admiral became unnerved and signaled his ships to withdraw. He had had enough, and radioed London that he could not go ahead unless he had the help of an army.

But a young Britisher, Commodore Roger Keyes, up front with the leading warships, did not want to quit. He went to Admiral de Robeck and pleaded that he be allowed to lead the mine sweepers. The Admiral was not happy about the idea, but he gave in to Roger Keyes' enthusiasm.

Keyes and his daredevils started at night. But the Turks, working to repair their damaged forts, were alert and turned on their searchlights. Belts of fire lashed out from the forts. One British warship, protecting the helpless mine sweepers, roared back at the Turks. It was an eerie scene. The crews on the mine sweepers were terrified and pulled back. Roger Keyes did not give up. He asked for volunteer crews and obtained them, but the fire in the night was too much for many of the sailors, and although the mine sweepers did not sink they withdrew. Keyes was furious.

Churchill, trying to direct the fight from London, radioed that the fleet would "have to press hard for a decision." And when he heard about the failure of the mine sweepers, he sent more radio messages. To fighters on the scene it was exasperating to receive detailed instructions from a political leader almost halfway around the world.

Churchill was overly hopeful, for warships alone could not defeat a series of forts. But even if the warships had bulled their way through the Narrows and had sailed past Constantinople after bombarding it, opening the seaway for the Czar, it is doubtful if battleships alone could have knocked the brave Turks out of the war.

Four weeks followed before the next ill-fated British campaign. The Turks worked hard to repair the forts. In this period the German General Liman von Sanders, in command of 60,000 Turkish troops, placed his men on and about the Gallipoli peninsula and waited for any attack that might come.

Chapter 9

THE GALLIPOLI CAMPAIGN

W HEN the strongest man on the British War Council, Lord Kitchener, decided to send an army to fight at the Dardanelles, nobody opposed him. The man he selected for the job was an old soldier of sixty-two, Sir Ian Hamilton. Hamilton wore a mustache, and his friendly eyes and kindly smile were signals of his charming personality. He was surprised to receive orders to command the expedition. Because he had served under Kitchener, he knew that few questions were desired by the dictatorial "Lord K," as he called Kitchener.

When Sir Ian Hamilton rushed off to Gallipoli on a destroyer, he was ill-prepared. He had no maps. He knew little of the Gallipoli peninsula other than that it was rugged. Sir Ian did not know if there would be drinking water for his soldiers, nor did he know anything about the roads, nor did he have information about the numbers of Turks he might face. He accepted the situation into which he had been thrust calmly. Hamilton was an old empire-building British soldier. He was used to "making bricks without straw."

Sir Ian was on the scene when the ships bringing his 75,000 troops arrived at the Dardanelles, and the way he found the vessels loaded was a bad omen. Horses were on one ship, their harness on another. Field guns were not on the same ship as their ammunition, and so on. Sir Ian decided to take the entire expedition off to Egypt to reload the ships. When the force arrived there it was discovered that many things needed for the fight

63

were missing, such as trench mortars, hand grenades, and ord-nance supplies. Spies in Egypt watched the force and gathered information about it, for they paid for information like this in Constantinople.

By the time Sir Ian had overcome numberless problems and set sail for waters off the Dardanelles, General Liman von Sanders and the fierce Turkish fighter, Mustafa Kemal, were ready and waiting. Rows of barbed-wire entanglements choked the beaches on the Gallipoli peninsula. Turkish troops were in trenches with guns sighted, and reserves were in locations from which they could rush to oppose the landings.

The guns of the Royal Navy helped the British soldiers fool the Turks by thundering at the beaches in the Gulf of Xeros, and so did the French, by landing at Kum Kale.[1] The Turkish sol-diers were mystified. They did not know where the main land-ings would take place.

Lieutenant Commander Bernard Freyberg helped in the hoax by swimming ashore at midnight in the icy water of the Gulf of Xeros, with a bag full of flares. He lit them along a stretch of beach a mile long, to give the Turks the impression they were guiding lights for the landing. Now "Barney" Freyberg faced the hardest part of his daring exploit. He waded into the sea and swam out into the darkness, hoping to be picked up. He had no light, and the cutter searching for him could risk none. When he was almost exhausted the small boat fortunately located him and hauled him aboard. Freyberg was awarded the Distinguished Service Order for this daring exploit.

The British soldiers landed at five beaches. At the very place where the British wished to put ashore the most soldiers, V Beach, the Turkish fire was the hottest. Here the English beached an old vessel, the *River Clyde*. It had holes cut in its sides, and gangways which could be lowered quickly. The idea was that the heavily laden infantrymen (each man wore a pack weighing eighty-eight pounds) would pour out of the holes and dash down the gangways. But when the *River Clyde* crunched onto

[1] See Map No. 8, page 60.

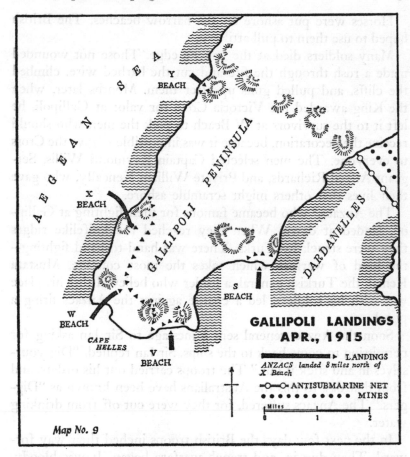

GALLIPOLI LANDINGS
APR., 1915

▶ LANDINGS
ANZACS landed 8 miles north of X Beach
—○—○— ANTISUBMARINE NET
•••••• MINES

Miles
0   1   2

Map No. 9

the beach, Turkish rifle and machine-gun fire beat a tattoo against the iron hull of the ship. The Turks had the range, and when the infantrymen appeared the result was slaughter. The color of the sea around the ship changed to red.

At W Beach, the 1st Battalion of the 20th Regiment of Lancashire Fusiliers was towed ashore. The Turks opened up with machine guns which had been carefully hidden. It was a case of gaining a foothold on the beach so they could scale the cliffs and stop the murderous fire. There could be no turning back. There never is in a landing on a hostile shore.

Horses were put ashore on the narrow beaches. The British hoped to use them to pull artillery.

Many soldiers died at the water's edge. Those not wounded made a rush through the fire and cut the barbed wire, climbed the cliffs, and pulled guns up after them. Months later, when the King awarded the Victoria Cross for valor at Gallipoli, he left it to the survivors at W Beach to pick the men who should receive the decoration, because it was impossible to give the Cross to everyone. The men selected Captain Raymond Willis, Sergeant Alfred Richards, and Private William Keneally, who gave their lives that others might scramble ashore.

The Anzacs,[2] who became famous for their fighting at Gallipoli, landed at dawn. When they reached the knifelike ridges they were struck by Turks. There was hand-to-hand fighting— the kind of warfare which takes the most courage. Mustafa Kemal, the Turkish general, a leader who believed that his place was with his soldiers, led a charge against the Anzacs firing a pistol.

Soon the Anzac general sent a message to Sir Ian asking for permission to come back to the ships. Sir Ian replied, "Dig yourselves in and stick it out." The troops carried out his orders, and from that day to this the Australians have been known as "Diggers." The Anzacs suffered, for they were cut off from drinking water.

In the next few days the British troops inched their way forward. They dug in, and trench warfare began. It was bloody, close combat.

By this time the narrow beaches were in confusion. Supplies crowded them from the cliffs to the water's edge. Huge guns were towed ashore on rafts and their gunners were hard put to it to find a place to put the cannons ashore. The organization for transporting the wounded back to ships was poor. The wounded lay on stretchers or on the sand, in rows, while Turkish artillery fire bathed them in iron. When the wounded were transported

---

[2] "Anzac" stood for Australian-New Zealand Army Corps.

to the ships, it was discovered that the doctors had gone to the beaches.

Drinking water brought ashore soon ran out and the troops thirsted. They found no springs or wells. Frantic messages were sent to the battleships for water. They sent it, but had to replenish their own supplies from islands fifteen and sixty-five miles away and from Egypt, 700 miles across the Mediterranean.

General Sir Ian Hamilton, in his headquarters on the *Queen Elizabeth*, saw only part of the battle, and reports reaching him were incomplete. The generals with the attacking troops did not lead or push them. Consequently, the British thrust slowed down and eventually came to a standstill. Sir Ian referred to his separation from the battlefield as being "wrapped in cotton-wool." Sir Ian was brave enough, but if he moved into any one beachhead he was cut off from the others, and he had to maintain contact with the admiral. He needed communications equipment and he did not have it. On the contrary, the German general with the Turks, Liman von Sanders, and Mustafa Kemal were literally all over the battlefield. They made their leadership felt.

The British public did not know of the suffering and the loss of life at Gallipoli. Fighting in France, just across the Channel, gripped the headlines. Then, too, an event of world-shaking importance occurred in May, 1915.

The British liner *Lusitania*, en route from New York City to Liverpool, was steaming along off the Irish coast, unaware that she was shadowed by a German U-boat. The captain of the U-20 gauged his distance. When he was ready he sent two torpedoes crashing into the side of the ship without warning. In twenty minutes the big ship sank to the bottom, carrying 1,150 men, women, and children with her, as well as $735,579 worth of copper, brass, and ammunition for the English armies. One hundred and fourteen Americans drowned. Public opinion in the United States blazed. The Kaiser sent a message to America expressing his deepest sympathy. President Wilson sent notes back demanding that German attacks on shipping cease. Relations between the two countries became strained. The frightful sinking of the *Lusitania* by a German submarine was a landmark in history.

But out at Gallipoli news of submarine attacks in the Atlantic and fighting in Flanders seemed worlds away. The Allies in Gallipoli gained little more than a few hard-earned yards by each attack. Their soldiers were exhausted. Sir Ian radioed word of the situation to "Lord K" and asked for more heavy ammunition. Back came an answer urging Sir Ian to "push on." He made a timid request for more men, received them, and landed at Suvla Bay.[3] The result: 18,000 more British died. One man wrote, "We have landed and dug another graveyard."

But for a while the spirit of the Allied soldiers and sailors in the Gallipoli-Dardanelles fight was buoyed by the feat of Lieutenant Commander Boyle. Edward Boyle was the skipper of the Royal Navy submarine E-14. This daring leader sailed his ship under mine fields into the Sea of Marmora and sank two Turkish gunboats and a transport loaded with Turkish soldiers. He was recommended for the Victoria Cross.

Lieutenant Commander Martin Nasmith, skipper of the E-11, set his square jaw, took his sub down, and headed for the Turkish mine fields. Like Boyle, he was gambling that his conning tower would not strike a mine. When the commander figured he was in the Sea of Marmora, he surfaced. Not far away was a Turkish sailing vessel. The young submarine skipper had imagination. He captured the Turkish sailship, lashed his sub to her, and began to hunt. He fooled a Turkish gunboat, an enemy transport, and several smaller craft, all of which he sent to the bottom.

At one time on her voyage into Turkish waters, Commander Nasmith's submarine was so close to shore she was chased by Turkish cavalry. Another time she shelled a camel caravan carrying supplies to the Gallipoli peninsula. Nasmith's underwater boat sank ship after ship, some of them so close to Constantinople that people in the streets saw the ships go down. Later, the E-11

[3] See Map No. 8, page 60.

sank the ancient Turkish battleship, *Barbarossa Harradin*. Martin Nasmith, like Edward Boyle, earned the Victoria Cross.

But the British were not the only daring undersea men. While the E-11 was driving to distraction the captains of Turkish gunboats who were hunting day and night for her, a German submarine traveled 3,300 miles from the North Sea to the Dardanelles in forty-two days. This was an unusual voyage for 1915. Two weeks after the German sub arrived, it sent to the bottom the British battleships *Goliath* and *Majestic*, and a transport carrying 900 soldiers.

The Royal Navy withdrew the *Queen Elizabeth* from the Dardanelles. To the British soldiers struggling with Turks, mountainous terrain, flies, and dysentery, this meant that the Navy was losing heart. The situation looked black to them.

In May the heat brought out poppies and tulips beside the trenches. The stench of the dead bodies became unbearable. Short truces were arranged to bury the dead, and men on each side saw that the enemy was not as abominable as they had thought.

In London, "Lord K," at a meeting of the War Council, spoke in bitter language of the failure of the British Navy to sail through the Dardanelles. He also talked of the enormous expenditure of ammunition with nothing but a few hundred yards of rocky ridges to show for it. In nine months of fighting the casualties of each side totaled about 250,000 men. Lord Fisher, the senior admiral on the War Council, said he had been against the Dardanelles campaign from the start. The idea of battleships being sent again through Turkish mine fields and battery fire upset Sir John Fisher. He was dead against it. He wrote angrily to Winston Churchill, "You are bent on forcing the Dardanelles and nothing will turn you from it—NOTHING."

Lord Fisher resigned in a huff. His friendship with Winston Churchill ended. The British Prime Minister, Mr. Asquith, begged the old admiral to return to the War Council. The admiral wrote an impossible memorandum, demanding as his "price" for returning, complete authority over the British Navy and its war at sea. His resignation was accepted. The British formed another government and the new Prime Minister, Lloyd George, removed Winston Churchill from his post as First Sea Lord.

Summer slipped by with the Turks and British locked in a death grip. "Lord K" removed Sir Ian from command, and the day Sir Ian departed for England the sailors on the British warships stood at attention on the decks and cheered for him.

A new general, Sir Charles Monro, was sent by Lord Kitchener to command the Gallipoli expedition. Monro took a quick look at the situation. Winter was at hand, but warm clothing for the soldiers was not, and there was a shortage of heavy ammunition. Monro sent "Lord K" a radio recommending that the expedition be withdrawn, adding that leaving in the face of the enemy would cost the lives of 40,000 men. Kitchener was shocked. He wondered if he had not made a mistake in selecting Sir Charles.

The old fire-eater, "Lord K," traveled to the Dardanelles and to the peninsula to see for himself. He went ashore and saw the miserable trenches and the almost impossible situation. He decided to end the campaign.

The British soldiers saw at once that they had a problem. If the Turks knew they were leaving, they could attack and slaughter them on the beaches and, while they were close to shore, in the small boats. So, along parts of their line, the British fooled the Turks with a trick. They drove stakes in the ground near some of their machine guns. Two buckets were hung from each stake, one over the other. The top bucket was full of water, but had small holes in it. The lower bucket was tied by a string to the trigger of the machine gun. When water leaked from the top bucket to the lower, the bottom bucket became heavy. It sank and pulled the trigger. The roar of the guns and the zip of the bullets made the Turks believe that the English were still in their trenches, while actually they were hurrying to the beaches. Along other parts of the line, brave men stayed behind so there would be some aimed fire at the Turks. These men left at the last possible minute. The withdrawal to the boats was the most brilliant part of a sad affair.

The leadership for the Allies, especially that on the spot with the soldiers, was poor. The judgment of the leaders in charge was wretched. They lacked force. The entire operation was costly and degrading. The campaign was one of the great disasters in British history.

Experts in the United States Navy wrote that it was doubtful if Great Britain could survive another Winston Churchill, but Churchill refused to stay down. He was to become the great leader of the English in the Second World War.

While the struggle on the Gallipoli Peninsula was going on, stalemate gripped the Western Front. The Germans and the Allies were stopped by each other's trenches, by the men who occupied them, and by their weapons—particularly the machine guns.

Chapter 10

DEADLOCK; TRAGEDY IN
SERBIA AND IN THE DESERT

THE British General Sir John French decided to "do his share" in breaking the deadlock. Sir John believed in fighting in the accepted way. He copied the German style of attack. The place was Neuve Chapelle, in northern France.

Sir John brought up 400 cannons and put them behind the British trenches. His idea was to bombard and destroy the German barbed wire in front of their positions, to wipe out their machine-gun nests, and to "flatten out" their trenches. It was 1915; the March weather was raw.

When the battle started, the roar of the bombardment and the clouds of earth shooting into the air made the scene seem like Hell itself. To the British standing on the fire steps of their trenches gazing across No Man's Land through homemade periscopes, it seemed as if the Germans must be wiped out. Surely no living thing could stand such a rain of iron.

The British Tommies from England, soldiers from Nepal— the Gurkhas—and other men from India readied themselves for a whistle signal. When it came they went "over the top."

The curtain of artillery fire gave the British some success, but the Germans did not quit. They manned their machine guns and fought bravely. Some German officers, who were just as reckless as any British leader walking across No Man's Land twirling a swagger stick, dashed up on horseback to lead counterattacks. Dead horses added to the horror. The idea of using horses near the trenches was quickly abandoned by the Germans.

The British were not the only ones who went over the top in a devil-may-care manner. In one attack a jaunty French leader, Capitaine Didelot, led his men out of a trench. A painting of the scene, hanging in Paris, shows the captain with three medals pinned to the chest of his blue-gray uniform. Although bullets are cutting down French soldiers at his side, the captain is striding toward the barbed wire. His fierce red mustache is bristling. He is encouraging his men by beckoning with his swagger stick.

The leaders missed no opportunity to inspire their soldiers. When General Marchand, of the French Army, was wounded, he ordered the four stretcher bearers to place his stretcher on their shoulders and to carry him back of the lines through groups of his soldiers who were waiting for the attack order. The sight of their general, white-faced and suffering, angered the French infantrymen.

But more than bravery was needed. Sir John French's attack at Neuve Chapelle bogged down. His walrus-like, white mustache could not hide the grim set of his mouth. He was disappointed. His men fought hard, but they dented the German lines for only 1,000 yards. Five hundred and forty-four British officers were killed or wounded, and twice that number of men in ranks.

In central Europe, battle news for the Allies was far worse. French attacks brought small gains, but 240,000 French soldiers were killed, wounded, or missing.

At St. Mihiel, French soldiers swept across No Man's Land. Papa Joffre had ordered, "Wear down the enemy." This, too, was a bloody failure.

The Allied generals on the Western Front decided that the thing to do was to attack together. But before they could do this the Germans attacked at Ypres, in Flanders, Belgium—territory they had failed to conquer. "Wipers," the Tommies called the place. The German idea was to straighten out their lines.[1] They now tried a new horror: poison gas.

Some survived the terrible yellow-green clouds by filling their handkerchiefs with damp earth and placing them across their faces. French infantry and African troops, fighting for France, panicked and ran to the rear. Many artillery gun crews died.

Behind the gas clouds marched German infantry, bayonets fixed. Some wore primitive gas masks on their faces. The Germans were afraid of their own gas. They were not aggressive. In the confusion, the Germans headed for a four-mile gap in the lines. It looked like a German breakthrough, but the Kaiser's generals lacked the reserves to push through the gap.

News of the poison gas horrified people of the Allied world. The Germans were pictured as Huns. A few Americans wondered if they should not be in the war to "save civilization." But there was also a strong element in the United States determined to keep our country out of the war.

A few months after the attack, the King of England awarded Victoria Crosses to five Canadians and to an English aviator who fought at Ypres. The heroism of the Canadian Colour Sergeant William Hall was typical of that of many soldiers on both sides. William Hall gave his life by rushing through enemy fire to save a wounded man who was crying for help in No Man's Land.

The pilot, Second Lieutenant William Rhodes-Moorhouse, had flown over a railroad station behind the German lines in western Belgium. He dropped his bombs accurately and was wounded. In the torment of his wounds Moorhouse had one thought: to fly back and tell the squadron about the antiaircraft guns now in position at Bruges. He flew thirty-five miles, just above the treetops, back to his airdrome, where he gave information about the enemy guns before he died.

But neither bravery by the soldiers nor thought by the generals

[1] See Map No. 15, page 155.

could break the stalemate on the Western Front. The trench systems facing each other stretched for hundreds of miles, gripping No Man's Land in a lock of steel. Today we can see the reason for the failure of the straight-ahead attacks better than the generals could at that time.

Weapons in use gave advantage to the defender rather than to the attacker. A machine gun could lay a stream of bullets along the barbed wire of a defensive position, and neither man nor beast could survive the bullets. Yet soldiers attacked. Attack was supposed to win. That was an accepted maxim. But machine guns and automatic rifles aided the defenders more than the attackers. The head-on attacks of 1915 brought the Allies dead men, disappointment, and disillusionment.

At about the time of the gas attack at Ypres, Italy entered the war on the Allied side. This was a new hope for the Allies. Italy demanded parts of Austria, and of course Austria refused to surrender her territory. Another country was added to the world war.

The leaders of the Allies prayed that the Italians would break the discouraging deadlock on the Western Front. Guns, ammunition, and war supplies were sent, but the Allies were disappointed. Italy hardly affected the course of the war.

While straight-ahead attacks in France in 1915 were costing both sides thousands of men, the hard-looking German leader, Falkenhayn, stirred up the war in the Balkans. Leaders in Bulgaria had studied the war for over a year, then decided that their country would fight against the Allies. Both sides tried to entice the Bulgarians, but, in addition to wanting to be on the "winning side," her citizens were pro-German and hated the Serbs.

General von Falkenhayn led Germans, Austrians, and Bulgarians against the small mountainous country of Serbia. The Serbs were in a vise.

The Allies arrived too late, and in too small numbers, to help. The Serbian Army was forced to leave its country. This was a blow for its soldiers. They were transferred through the Adri-

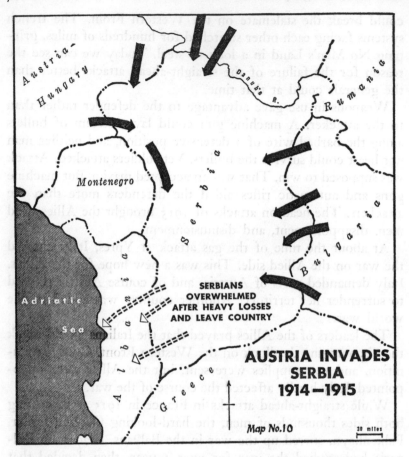

Map No. 10 — AUSTRIA INVADES SERBIA 1914–1915. SERBIANS OVERWHELMED AFTER HEAVY LOSSES AND LEAVE COUNTRY. 30 miles

atic Sea to Salonika, Greece. In the fighting there, neither side won. The real victor was malaria. In three years, 150,000 men suffered from the dread disease.

More bad news came for the Allies: the Austrians defeated the Italians in four battles. The Italians fought gamely, but 250,000 died, and Italy had little to show for this sacrifice.

In the fighting in the Italian Alps, one day there was excitement. A grenade belonging to the Italian Army exploded, wounding an Italian corporal, Benito Mussolini. Mussolini was well known in his country, for he was a showman, a radical politician, a newspaper editor, and a man who loved to shout, "There is no God." Four years after the war, Mussolini became head of the Italian government, and later helped bring on the Second World War.

While the country of Serbia was suffering, tragedy was occurring in the desert.

In late 1914 the British had sent soldiers to the head of the Persian Gulf. This was a key area because of oil in Persia. The British thought, too, that the appearance of their soldiers in Persia would encourage the Arabs to fight the Turks.

The British leader at the Persian Gulf was a general who saw no difficult problems in ordering soldiers into the Mesopotamian desert. This was Sir John Nixon. Without hesitation, he dispatched his soldiers 250 miles into the desert to seize a Turkish stronghold at a place called Kut, a name that would plague the British for years.

Sir John Nixon gave the job of leading the men into the desert to Major General Charles Townshend, who was even more unrealistic than Nixon. A hard fighter at times, General Townshend believed himself capable of any task. In his mind, all he had to do was to set the task and victory would follow.

Townshend sent planes to skim over the desert, and when they returned with information he captured the desert mud heap called Kut. It was a forlorn town. Baghdad, one hundred miles away, looked far more inviting. So General Townshend ordered his men farther into the desert.

The British Cabinet in London must bear some of the blame, for it pressed the idea of the strike into the desert on the two willing generals. Only Lord Kitchener thought that moving a greater distance into the barren country was a poor plan.

Just before Townshend marched toward the fabled city of Baghdad, he asked Sir John for more soldiers. But Nixon pooh-poohed the idea. "There are no Turks in the desert," he said.

Sixteen miles from Baghdad there was a fight, and Townshend's force was outnumbered by the Turks. Forty per cent of

BAGHDAD

PERSIA

KUT

MESOPOTAMIA

SYRIAN DESERT

Euphrates R.

Tigris R.

Oil Pipeline

MESOPOTAMIA—
1914 — 1917
A CAMPAIGN
ENDS AT KUT

Miles
0   100

FAO
British land
here

PERSIAN
GULF

Map No. II

Townshend's infantrymen were killed or wounded. The general ordered a retreat to Kut. In this miserable town most of the buildings were of clay bricks, without roofs, or with roofs of grass mats. There were few modern improvements.

For five months the Turks surrounded Kut. Townshend's supply officers doled the food out. It was scarce, and they were also feeding 6,000 Arabs in the town who did nothing to help.

The longer the siege lasted, the more unsanitary Kut became. The sick and wounded suffered and received improper care. Day by day the British ranks became thinner. Word leaked out about the garrison in Kut, and the entire world wondered what would happen.

General Nixon sent a relieving force. It was poorly organized. It had little medical equipment, and but one airplane.

More and more Turks came from the Dardanelles, because the British there had sailed for home. The Turks attacked and defeated Nixon's rescuing force. Rain and cold sent the hopes of the men shut up in Kut even lower. The Tigris River overflowed its banks and drowned numbers of British soldiers. The houses made of mud became mud again. Disease spread. The British tried dropping food from the sky to their soldiers in Kut, but they needed more planes.

Horsemeat was served, but Indian troops fighting alongside the British refused to eat it, for it was against their religion. Camel meat was hard to digest. Every day in Kut became a greater tragedy for the Allies.

Halil, the Turkish leader, promised the British that if they would surrender they would be his "guests." Townshend fell for Halil's treachery, and in 1916, in April, 10,000 British troops laid down their arms. The entire campaign cost Great Britain 40,000 men.

General Halil and his Turks treated their prisoners in unspeakable fashion. Among the things they did was to whip and beat British soldiers. They marched them long hours across the desert with little food or water. They placed them in filthy prison camps, tortured them, and murdered many. General Townshend, on the contrary, lived in captivity in fine fashion.

From Britain came more soldiers and a real leader, an Irishman, General Sir Stanley Maude. He was popular and he worked hard to care for his soldiers. He improved the food they ate; chicken and fresh eggs replaced canned meat. Maude won a second Battle of Kut. He outfought the Turks at every turn. But when things looked brightest, Maude died of cholera.

The British eventually won in Mesopotamia, but paid dearly. The loss of 92,000 soldiers of the King—many of them dying from disease—did not affect the course of the war, but the loss was a sign that British rule in the Middle East, two centuries old, was ending.

To the trials of the British was added the defeat of a British expeditionary force in German East Africa.

There were further command troubles, too, to plague the British. Sir John French was so irritable that people near him lost confidence in him. He was replaced by Sir Douglas Haig, who was also an experienced general. Haig was of splendid character. He was cool, determined, and had powerful friends, but some who knew him well wondered if he were brilliant enough for the very difficult task in the west of leading the British Army.

Things looked dark on the German side, too, but the German nation was far from defeated. The British Navy had blockaded its ports, but that alone could not defeat the Kaiser. The Germans were disappointed that the war was not won quickly. However, they believed they could win by the autumn of 1916.

The year 1916 saw even bigger battles and longer lists of killed, wounded and missing. But before these desperate fights, Zeppelins sailed the skies over England, and planes began to play more important parts.

Chapter 11

BRAVERY IN THE SKY

COUNT ZEPPELIN was a kindly German scientist who hoped that his invention of the airship bearing his name would be used in the cause of peace. When he was a young man, Ferdinand Zeppelin came to the United States as an observer with the Union Army in the Civil War. It is said that he obtained the idea of the Zeppelin while watching captive observation balloons near Fredericksburg.

The Zeppelin was a spectacular invention and it had an effect on the war, but not one anticipated by the Germans.

The best Zeppelins built by the Germans were 680 feet long, about the length of two and one-half football fields. They were seventy-two feet thick through the middle. Their framework was a light but strong aluminum alloy, tapered like a pencil. In addition to spacious crew compartments inside the ship, resembling the accommodations of a Pullman car, men on duty rode in two gondolas slung underneath. There was an observation car which could be lowered by a thousand feet of cable. This car, equipped with telephones, permitted an observer to travel under the clouds while the airship sailed above them.

The first bombs the Zeppelins dropped were artillery shells with blankets wrapped about one end to act as a "rudder" to insure that the shell fell point downward. Later, the fire, or incendiary, bombs were equipped with a collar of revolving fans to insure that the bomb fell on its point. A Zeppelin carried 300 fire bombs. The airships were armed with light cannon and

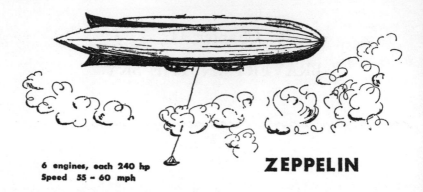

6 engines, each 240 hp
Speed 55 - 60 mph   **ZEPPELIN**

machine guns, and there were guns on top of the airship as well as in the gondolas. It took a brave pilot to attack a Zeppelin.

Although the Zeppelins had six engines which whirled the propellers, the ships could develop a speed of only sixty miles an hour. This, and the ship's bulk, made them awkward and hard to handle in a wind.

The idea of the Zeppelin raids against England was to bring the war home to the English. It was also hoped by the Germans that the big ships could drop enough incendiary bombs to set all of London afire and to paralyze English industry. But thinking Germans knew this was impossible.

When the first Zeps sailed over London, the British were not ready. They knew of Count Zeppelin's invention, but they hoped that the storms and rough weather that hung over the English Channel a large part of the year would protect them, and that if any Zeppelins got through the planes of the Royal Flying Corps could drive them off. The British visualized the airships attacking in daylight.

But the Germans attacked the city of London at night, in September of 1915, and there were thirteen airships in the sky. The Kaiser, in permitting the raid, had thoughtfully given instructions not to bomb his cousin, the King, in Buckingham Palace. But when the bombardiers dropped their fire bombs they had no idea where they would fall. The Zeppelin commanders did have one guidepost, no matter how dark the city: the River Thames. When the few searchlights the British had picked up the big cigar-like shadows in the sky, the sight of Zeppelins over England was more damaging to English nerves than the wreckage caused by the bombs.

The homes demolished and the women and children killed infuriated the British people. When news of the big raid struck the United States, many people thought that the Germans had sunk to a new low. Newspapers featured pictures of wrecked homes. The ghostly visitors accomplished what the most skilled recruiting sergeants were worrying about: persuading Englishmen to enlist. This was the biggest effect of the raids.

The British worked feverishly to develop their air defenses. Over London, balloon aprons—steel cables hung from captive balloons—were sent up. Better searchlights, and antiaircraft cannon which could reach far into the sky, were built. Squadrons of Bristol and Nieuport Scouts, R.E.5's, and Vickers F.B.5's, scheduled to be shipped to France, were held in England. The city practiced blackouts. When warning of a raid came, London police dashed through the streets in open touring cars which bore a sign in red letters: TAKE COVER. Sound signals howled the alarm. All lights were turned out. There were stories of spies on motorcycles equipped with flashlights who guided the Zeppelins to the city.

The searchlights sweeping the skies were so bright one could read a newspaper if in their beam twenty miles away. The Zeppelins stood out like targets at a shooting gallery. Red fire from the antiaircraft guns laced the sky, and some of the shells clattered back into the city, causing almost as much damage as the bombs.

It took courage to ride in a Zeppelin on a raid. Being shot at in the air was worse than the same experience on the ground. The battles between daring airmen and the brave gunners and crews on the Zeppelins were hair-raising. The hydrogen tanks which kept the Zeppelins aloft were inflammable, and the crews knew that it would take only a spark to send them crashing to earth in a flaming coffin. The crews knew, too, that if they were captured they could expect rough treatment. Sailors on an English trawler, fishing in the North Sea, saw a Zeppelin crash into the water. The trawler sailed by the wreck and men on her deck shouted, "We do not rescue Zeppelin crews." Dead Zeppelin airmen were honored by proper military funerals, with British airmen attending.

When the Zeppelins fought over Russia, the fate of captured Zeppelin crews was not as bad as that of airplane pilots captured by the Russians. Those unfortunates were shot. Captured Zeppelin crews were sent to prison camps in Siberia, where they were beaten and starved.

The pilots who battled the Zeppelins were national heroes of the British. On one raid, Flight Commander W. L. Robinson, twenty-one years old, was one of three airmen attacking a Zeppelin. Two of the pilots were driven off by bullets from the airship. Robinson kept coming, pumping tracer bullets into the Zeppelin until it crashed. Young Robinson received the Victoria Cross and a cash prize of about $17,500.

The Kaiser rewarded his heroes, too. He telegraphed Senior Lieutenant Horst Treusch: ... YOU HAVE, WITH FIVE OF MY AIRSHIPS, SUCCESSFULLY CARRIED OUT INNUMERABLE RECONNAISSANCE FLIGHTS AND FIFTEEN RAIDS. ... I INVEST YOU WITH THE ORDER POUR LE MÉRITE.

In August 1918, Captain F-K. Strasser, one of the Kaiser's best Zeppelin commanders, commanding the new L-70, a powerful Zeppelin, went down with his airship when a British airman attacked, firing incendiary bullets. These new bullets, which set the Zeppelins on fire, signaled their end.

There were about eighty-five Zeppelin raids. The toll was high due to counteraction, weather, and other causes. Fifty-two Zeppelins failed to return to their airdromes. The Germans raided London and Paris—not only with Zeppelins, but with airplanes. But in casualties, the total killed was not as great as one might expect. For instance, the number of Englishmen killed in all air raids was 1,413. Over 3,000 people were injured. The Zeppelins did not cause great damage, but they angered Englishmen, sending thousands enthusiastically to the Colors. In neutral countries men wondered what might happen to their own cities if the Germans won the war.

As the war went on planes began to play more important parts. Fast little Nieuport Scouts and Bristol Scouts began to appear in greater numbers. In them were British and French pilots. The Bristol pilots were armed with rifles or pistols. Later, the plane carried a Lewis machine gun. The Nieuport biplanes had machine guns mounted on the top wings which fired over the propellers.

The Nieuports handled well except when they were in a steep dive. Then, sometimes, their wings tore off. The tall, daring Irishman who became the top ace in the Royal Air Force, Major Edward (Mick) Mannock, decided to take up a Nieuport and dive it to see how steep the slope had to be before the wings tore away. He made each dive steeper. Finally, the fabric on one of the wings ripped off. Mannock managed to land in a plowed field. He passed the information on to others as best he could, but it was hard to be precise, for in 1915 planes had only two instruments: a bubble-level, to tell the pilot if one wing was higher than the other, and a compass. A leather cushion was placed over the cowl of the cockpit in the hope it would keep the aviator's teeth from being knocked out in a rough landing.

The Bristol Bullet and the Nieuport were able to stay up for two and one-half hours. The Bristol could make a speed of 104 miles an hour, while the Nieuport could zip along at 140. They needed all the speed they could get, for their enemies, the Fokkers, built their speed up from 90 to 124.

The Dutch inventor and plane manufacturer, Anthony Fokker, worked hard to improve his planes. He thought up the idea of having a machine gun set to fire through the propeller. The firing of the gun was timed so that the bullets would not hit the rotating blades. This gave the Germans an advantage, because all the pilot had to do was to aim his plane and pull the trigger. The Fokkers were monoplanes, biplanes, and triplanes. They were the best planes of 1915. They were so effective that young British pilots referred to themselves as "Fokker fodder."

The Fokkers, their wings braced by piano wire, were flown by aces whom Germans idolized, such as Oberleutnants Oswald Boelcke and Max Immelman. Every German knew how Boelcke had once rushed to his plane wearing only a helmet, boots, and a nightshirt, to go aloft and bring down a British plane. Boelcke was fearless and skillful. He shot down forty planes before he was killed in a flying accident.

But the first hero of the war was Immelman. It was Immelman who used to advantage the plane maneuver that bears his name, the Immelman turn. In a fight he would pull the stick back sharply, making the nose of his plane zoom upward. At the top of the circle, instead of looping, he executed a half-roll, whipping the plane about and flying off in the opposite direction.

The Fokkers, and the pilots flying them, made the great British fighter, Captain Albert Ball, and other daring RFC pilots, adopt formation flying. They had to fly in groups of at least three.

Acts of heroism were often acts of supreme sacrifice, born of a desire to demolish the enemy so the homeland could win. For instance, Lieutenant Floch and Sergeant Rodde, of the French Air Force, were bombing German-held towns back of the trenches when they were suddenly opposed by twenty-three Fokkers. Bullets whistling through the gas tank of the French plane set it on fire. The French airplane started to fall. Floch and his brave sergeant saw their chance. They still had control over their craft. They guided it into a Fokker and both planes crashed. Jacques Mortane wrote, ... *the victims carried along their conqueror.*

Some of the French pilots liked to ridicule their opponents. Captain Albert Heurtaux, who became chief of the famous Escadrille N.3, was a frozen-faced, expressionless young man. When he flew by in his Nieuport, he would sometimes wave his hand carelessly in greeting to a nearby German aviator, or he would stand up and bow. This infuriated the Germans. They replied with bullets and by shaking their fists. But the calm-looking captain was a better shot than most of his enemies. He was the first aviator to bring down an enemy plane with a single shot.

French pilot Adolphe Pégoud, the first man to "loop the loop" (he did it in 1912), was not afraid to fight anyone in the air as long as his mascot was along. This was a toy penguin, ten inches long, lashed to the wires of his plane. But one day over Alsace the penguin did no good; Pégoud and his Nieuport 210 were shot down. The Germans honored Pégoud by returning the toy penguin and by having white armbands printed for the funeral party. On the armbands in gold letters were the words: *FOR WHOM IN COMBAT FOR HIS FATHERLAND, THE FALLEN FLIER PÉGOUD IS HONORED BY HIS EN-EMIES.*

The Germans had time for chivalry, and it even appeared in one of the worst battles in the history of the world: Verdun.

Chapter 12
VERDUN—"THEY SHALL NOT PASS"

~~~~~~

I N 1916 a battle was fought that drew men to it as though it were some kind of fiendish magnet. It was fought at Verdun.

Many people think of the amazing Battle of Verdun as a fight for an old-time fort. The town did once stand inside a Roman fortress and, later, when the town grew and the walls were extended, Verdun became a fortified city. But, before World War I, French generals decided that the best way to defend the key area of Verdun was to build a ring of forts about it, eight miles from the town. The bitter fight for these forts occupied ten square miles.

Americans remember the Battle of Gettysburg, which lasted three days. About 163,000 men were involved and approximately 7,000 of them died. The tremendous Battle of Verdun lasted eleven months. The losses were staggering. The Germans poured over a million men into the battle, losing 434,000. More and more Frenchmen were rushed to the defense of Verdun, and 542,000 were killed, wounded, or missing. With 976,000 men lost, the battle has rightfully been called "one of history's greatest slaughters."

The Germans knew that Verdun was the pride of France. General Falkenhayn was certain that an attack upon it would cause the French to rush to its defense, and that France could be "bled white" there, forcing her to seek peace. The general also reasoned that, by smashing Verdun, he could prevent a French attack from that point. In order to gain even greater

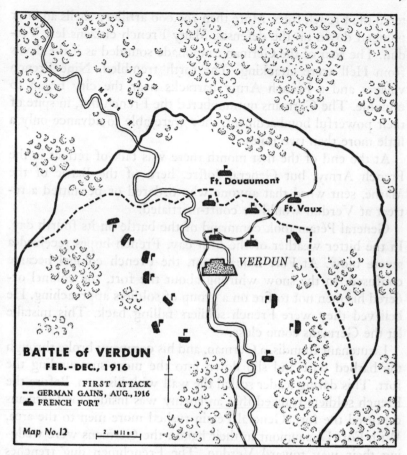

BATTLE of VERDUN
FEB.-DEC., 1916

FIRST ATTACK
-- GERMAN GAINS, AUG., 1916
⚓ FRENCH FORT

Map No. 12   2 Miles

advantage from the expected victory, the Kaiser's son, Crown Prince Wilhelm, was placed in command. A win would restore prestige to the royal family.

The Crown Prince decided that the way to victory lay in curtains of artillery fire. Therefore he placed over a thousand guns on the line in front of Verdun. While the fight at Verdun was not of strategic brilliance, it became more important each month because of the tremendous numbers of men killed.

The German attack, starting in February 1916, signaled the zero hour for Verdun. For twelve hours German artillery battered the French forts. More than 100,000 artillery shells an hour plunged down on the defenses. Many French citizens left Verdun. The roar of the German cannonade sounded as if the devils from Hell were attacking. The earth trembled. Nine French villages and a French Army barracks near the city began to crumble. The Germans outnumbered the French but, in spite of their powerful bombardment, they were able to advance only a little more than two miles.

At the end of the first month there was talk of retreat in the French Army, but General Joffre, hero of the Battle of the Marne, sent word that anyone who ordered or permitted a retreat at Verdun would be court-martialed.

General Pétain took command of the battle on its fourth day. In the bitter weather of the fifth day, French hopes received a severe blow. At Fort Douaumont, the French colonel became confused. In the snow whirling about the fort, the colonel ordered his men not to fire on a group of soldiers approaching. He believed they were French soldiers falling back. This mistake let the Germans come close.

Lieutenant Brandis, a German, and his company broke through the barbed wire and slid down into the moat surrounding the fort. This daring leader scaled the wall with his men. Before the French soldiers realized that an enemy was inside, the Germans captured the fort. General Pétain rushed more men to the area. With Fort Douaumont in their hands, the Germans were wedging their way toward Verdun. The Frenchmen dug trenches under fire to stop them.

General Pétain worked long hours under pressure. Later in the battle his nerve broke. He wanted to move everyone out of the ring of forts and give the city to the Germans. Old Papa Joffre stiffened him. Joffre told Pétain to "hold to the job." However, Pétain must be given credit for fine leadership at Verdun. Under him the Battle of Verdun became a crusade. He made the French have faith. To this day Frenchmen living in and near Verdun have revered him. He made them believe that the Germans must not pass.

The question of supply became vital to the French. The Germans were able to send fresh men, more ammunition, food, guns, clothing, and medicine to the battle, and to bring back the wounded, because they had fourteen railways available. The French were handicapped. As supply routes they had only one regular and one narrow-gauge railroad, plus a narrow macadam road. This road, soon known to the French as the "Sacred Way," was burdened with traffic. At its busiest time, a vehicle of some sort passed over it every fourteen seconds.

The Germans quickly caught on to the value to their enemy of the Sacred Way and raked it with artillery fire. The scenes on the narrow Sacred Way were terrible: fire, death, drivers determined to get their vehicles through, road repair under fire, the wounded wounded again, supplies scattered in the ditches and over the road—but somehow the traffic rolled on. Today in France the Sacred Way is the only road not numbered in the system of highways. Its milestones are marked, instead of with numbers, with the ridged steel helmet of the French soldier.

The Germans faced a decision. They had not won. Should they renew the attack or fight the British? They knew from captured prisoners that in the Somme area, one hundred and twenty miles to the north of Verdun, the British were ready to attack. Falkenhayn decided to pour more men into the Battle of Verdun. He and the Crown Prince continued their special tactic: each German unit had a specified place to capture. First, German artillery would pound and pound the French area to be captured. Next, German scouts rushed forward to gather reports on the effect of the artillery fire and to gain information on the French left in the trenches. Then came rows of pioneers, as wirecutters, accompanied by "bombers" carrying hand grenades which they threw. In single file, next came the infantry. After them, reserves carrying ammunition, sandbags, spare weapons. And during this chainlike, machine movement, German artillery rained down on French trenches, blotting out machine guns and killing men brave enough to fire their weapons.

At one place, perhaps more, French soldiers were smothered

to death when German artillery caved in the sides of their trench, the chalklike earth burying men alive, leaving only their bayonets sticking above ground to mark the line of the trench.

General Pétain rushed more troops into the battle, placing them as best he could to stop the machine-like attacks. Someone said, "*Ils ne passeront pas.*" This cry, "They shall not pass," became the fighting slogan of the French at Verdun. The French again stopped the enemy.

General Falkenhayn could not sleep at night, for he lived with a terrible problem. Not only was he losing men, but the French army about Verdun had now been greatly reinforced. If he stopped the battle and withdrew, they might counterattack. The Crown Prince joined him, his gawky neck craned forward over the battle map. Crown Prince Wilhelm persuaded Falkenhayn that he could win if fresh troops were brought up and placed in the attack. "Besides," the Crown Prince said, "the new poison-gas shells carrying phosgene will kill thousands of Frenchmen."

The German Crown Prince sent his men down the west bank of the Meuse River. His artillery rained down every type of shell: shells which exploded in the air, shells that hurled steel balls at the infantry below, shells which burst when they hit the ground, shells which carried tear gas, and shells which were loaded with phosgene and other kinds of poisonous gas.

Never have Frenchmen fought harder. In a trench at a place called Dead Man Hill, nine miles northwest of the town, four colonels and a brigadier general took their places, pistols in hand, alongside their soldiers, to die fighting. German soldiers, too, died trying to go forward.

The battle pushed on into late May, 1916. The Germans now attacked down the east bank of the Meuse River. The bodies of their brave men dotted the shell-pocked land. The area became more desolate with each barrage and counterbarrage. The trees disappeared. The earth took on the appearance of the moon's surface when viewed through a telescope. Through it all, at the head of the determined French army, stood General Pétain. He encouraged the French soldiers to hang on to their ground. General Robert Nivelle was one of Pétain's best subordinates, and he did fine work. Similarly, the Germans put in the best generals they could, to help the Crown Prince.

The tall Crown Prince ordered an all-out attack toward Fort Vaux. At this turtle-back, concrete fort the French had the best type of defense: determined defenders. Their leader was Major Jean Raynal, a chubby man with piercing blue eyes. The German massed infantry, suffering great casualties, overpowered the fort. The concrete walls were rubble. They had received 8,000 shells a day for three months.

But Major Raynal was a stubborn defender. He decided to stay. He sent most of his men to Verdun, keeping a few to resist until the end. In order to do this, Major Raynal and the soldiers who volunteered to stay with him went underground.

The Germans swarmed over the little concrete fort. They congratulated each other on the fort's capture. A scout, peering into an underground passage, was shot dead.

The Germans thought that perhaps there was one Frenchman underground, but soon they saw the problem: they had captured only the top of the fort; the tunnels and quarters underneath were filled with Frenchmen. Some place the number of men who stayed with Major Raynal as low as 125, some as high as 250.

The main attack continued to inch ahead, but hundreds of Germans stayed to ferret out the fighters under Fort Vaux. First, the Germans gassed the underground passages. Next, they shot liquid flame down into the dark corridors. But Major Raynal and his men held. The French leader and his soldiers suffered under horrible conditions, but they would not quit. Water became precious. To drink, a man had to snatch off his gas mask, hold his breath, and gulp quickly. Food ran out. Thirst was worse than hunger. One of Raynal's men, Sergeant Aime Clairond, wrote, *My throat burned for water. Where I was, there were sixty of us. We divided the dirty water by the spoonful.*

Major Raynal sent carrier pigeons bearing messages written on tissue paper and clamped to the pigeons' legs in aluminum capsules. He hoped the Germans could be swept away from the top of the fort by a counterattack.

In spite of tortures of thirst, hunger, and unbelievable living conditions, Jean Raynal and his soldiers fought on. The men were willing to stay because their leader stayed and because he filled them with hope. On the sixth day of the underground battle all food gave out. Near the end of the eighth day Major Raynal penned a message in shaky handwriting: *We have reached the limit. Officers and men have done their duty. Long Live France!*

The Germans saw a Frenchman thrust the pigeon out of a window. Gas was sprayed toward the bird. It was shot at, too, yet it flew to its loft in the town hall in Verdun. There it died. The message inspired the French, but they could not break through the ring of Germans to rescue the men entombed in Fort Vaux.

Raynal and his men finally surrendered. It was the eighth day of their heroic fight. They staggered above ground and laid down their weapons. So impressed were the Germans by Major Raynal's courage that they let him keep his ceremonial sword, which he wore in captivity. The Germans stood at attention while Major Raynal and his surviving men were marched away as prisoners.

The Germans sent 200,000 poison-gas shells onto two ridges north of Verdun. Huge "beer-barrel" shells set the ridges and valley between on fire. "The Furnace," Frenchmen called the area, but they held on to it.

The nine French villages in the area, and the French Army post, were blotted out. The city of Verdun was a shambles, yet the French held.

The German government now decided that Falkenhayn had failed. They replaced him with the HL team—Hindenburg and Ludendorff. Their first order was to stop the attack. The French, under the command of a dynamic leader, General Charles Mangin, now started forward. They regained Fort Douaumont and Fort Vaux and captured 9,000 Germans.

President Raymond Poincaré of France traveled to Verdun

and decorated the city with the Grand Cross of the Legion of Honor, for Verdun and its churned and pock-marked fields symbolized the determination of the French people. Heroes were decorated. Even the pigeon who flew Major Raynal's last message from Fort Vaux received the Croix de Guerre medal.

Neither side won the battle. In the eleven months of fighting 976,000 soldiers were killed, wounded, or captured. The battle was one in which both sides suffered terribly. General Hindenburg wrote, "The Battle of Verdun exhausted our forces like a wound that never heals." The stubborn defense and great sacrifice by the French Army inspired the French nation.

Today visitors from all over the world travel to Verdun. Relics of the battle are treasured in the town hall, and monuments dot the battlefield. The descendants of the Frenchmen who lost their homes in the nine villages make an annual pilgrimage to the desolate area where their homes once stood. On the battlefields, one can almost hear the mystic rallying cry, "They shall not pass."

Chapter 13

SLAUGHTER ON THE SOMME

THE pressure on the Allies in 1916 was so great that the leaders held a conference. They planned to attack on the Western, Italian, and Eastern fronts, all at the same time. But the German attack at Verdun upset the Allies' plans.

Papa Joffre hoped by having the British attack at the Somme River to draw the Germans away from the Hell at Verdun. He also hoped to break through the German lines and go all the way to the Rhine. The battlefield Joffre selected—the Somme—did him no credit.[1] There had been no fighting there for two years, and the Germans were well prepared.

The Germans had worked like beavers in those two years to strengthen their lines there. They built row upon row of trenches. Miles of stout barbed-wire entanglements guarded their trenches. Deep concrete dugouts were available for front-line and support troops. Pillboxes, small concrete houses neatly dug into the earth so they were partly hidden, housed machine guns and crews. They dotted the landscape. The machine gunners, and battery officers of artillery located farther back, knew the ranges to every point on the ground.

To ready his army for the battle, General Haig spaced 1,500 cannons along an eighteen-mile front. The French, who were to help, had even more artillery. Mountains of shells were hauled by truck and horse to the guns. Haig was a cavalryman, and now that he thought there was a good chance of a breakthrough, he

[1] See Map No. 15, page 155.

placed cavalry in spots where it could wait his signal to gallop through the hole and cut up the German rear areas. Haig was pleased before the attack because British pilots controlled the air over No Man's Land.

Sir Douglas Haig tried to fool the Germans before the fight started by trying to make them think that he was going to attack elsewhere. He sent extra men and artillery farther north.

In June 1916, the Allied artillery began the battle. The earth trembled from the bombardment. Showers of dirt and steel fragments sprayed the German trenches. In one place the Allied artillerymen used a "creeping barrage." This was a curtain of shells that moved into German territory ahead of the Allied infantry. But it was not well timed. The attacking infantrymen fell far behind it. The Germans went underground when the bombardment began, and when it moved away the Kaiser's men in the dugouts raced for their positions in the trenches. Because the Allied infantrymen were not close to the barrage, the Germans had time to aim and shoot.

Sixty thousand British soldiers died on the first day of the battle. On each following day, more soldiers were killed on both sides.

The young men who died for the King and Country were the cream of Great Britain. They were volunteers. Many of them were football players, cricket players, track athletes, boys who had gone to school together. They were a band of brothers, brave and eager to win.

The trees in the Somme battlefield soon became nude stumps. The torn and jagged woods seemed to be symbols of the hopelessness of the attack. But it was not Sir Douglas Haig's nature to quit. The battle went on in grim, grinding agony.

Suddenly, on the twentieth day, Allied infantrymen fought their way through the German defense lines. Haig, a man of little joy or humor, permitted himself a ray of happiness. He and his headquarters were filled with hope. Telephone messages brought the cavalrymen up so they could push through the hole. Then the false picture crashed; German reserves appeared and counterattacked. The wounded and dead horses on the battlefield added to the horror. The Allies lost ground.

It was at this time that a new invention appeared on the battlefield. It was a mechanical monster designed to help the fighters who bore the heaviest burden in each battle—the infantrymen. But before the mechanical monster could overcome German machine guns, a series of obstacles behind the lines had to be overcome, and much work had to be done.

The invention was called "the tank" as a secret code name. Colonel Ernest D. Swinton, a slender, distinguished-looking officer who sported a gray mustache, was its inventor. In 1914, Colonel Swinton received orders to report in person to Lord Kitchener in the War Office in London. Swinton, a Regular officer of the Royal Engineers, had known "Lord K" in South Africa during the Boer War. There Swinton saw British infantry attack the Boers, the world's finest marksmen, with bad results.

In the War Office, Colonel Swinton found Lord Kitchener friendly but brief. After a few pleasantries, "Lord K" glared at the trim officer and said, "Swinton, I want you to go to France as a writer-observer. Check in with General French, of course. But send reports to me. I want to know how they're fighting— both sides. You are not to spy, but I want information. If your articles are any good—they'll come to me personally—I'll send them on to the press. I may chop out a thing or two. If there are no questions, that's all. Thank you for coming in."

In France, Colonel Swinton reported to Sir John French. Swinton found the British leader nervous and irritable. The idea of having a military reporter around writing up the fighting did not sit well with the old general. "Are you here to spy on me and my soldiers?" French barked.

"No, sir," Swinton said. "I'm here to give Lord Kitchener and the public a picture of what our men are doing, how they fight, and how the Germans fight."

"The public! Humph!"

Shortly after Colonel Swinton persuaded the crotchety general that he should be allowed to go to the front, Swinton saw the problem—but not the answer. The slaughter was far worse than anything he had seen in the Boer War. When machine guns swept the battlefield with a ghastly clatter, infantrymen died by the score.

For days Swinton pondered. "What can be done to help the infantrymen across No Man's Land and on into German territory?"

Swinton wrote his reports and sent them to "Lord K," who, in turn, forwarded many of them to the newspapers, but the big problem in Swinton's mind was not discussed. It was how to overcome the machine gun. Finally, he thought of an agricultural American Caterpillar tractor he had once seen in Belgium. He went to see the fighting there.

The Battle of Ypres, 1914, was under way when Colonel Swinton arrived. The British dead on the battlefield scourged him on. He wrote a report and sent it to the War Council. His idea was that a track-laying caterpillar vehicle, armored and carrying a gun to knock out enemy machine guns, could "walk" across No Man's Land and help the infantrymen forward.

Swinton's first disappointment was "Lord K" himself. Kitchener was unenthusiastic about the idea. Other senior British generals were irritated by Swinton's "tank." Some said he had not submitted the idea properly, and others said it just would not work, that it was impracticable. Colonel Swinton's sense of humor kept him operating, pushing in person in London to get his idea approved. Fortunately, Winston Churchill, at that time still First Lord of the Admiralty, became interested. Although the army scorned the tank, Mr. Churchill adopted it.

Churchill got behind the idea with all his marvelous energy, and consequently the British Navy developed the first tank. They called it a "land battleship."

Slowly, Colonel Swinton's idea took shape. He experimented with armor plate, borrowing a captured German machine gun and firing bullets into it. He wanted to find out how thick the armor had to be to stop a bullet. It would be senseless to have the tank carry more weight than it had to.

Secrecy surrounded the construction of the first tank. It was decided that the vehicle should have caterpillar tracks, that the armor plate should be four-tenths of an inch thick in front and three-tenths of an inch thick on the sides, and that there should be a six-pounder gun aboard serviced by a crew of eight. Some tanks had machine guns. The speed varied from three miles per hour to six.

Lord Kitchener, his staff, and senior generals were invited to watch the first "tank trials." Also present were Prime Minister Lloyd George and top political leaders of England. Colonel Swinton felt nervous. He was afraid something would go wrong. Fortunately, the trials proceeded smoothly. The tank eased itself across a nine-foot ditch and withstood the fire of a German machine gun. Senior persons rode in it. Swinton's happiness spread over his face. Then Lord Kitchener said, "Poof! The idea is a toy."

But King George saw and liked the tank. He told Swinton that thousands should be manufactured. The general staff was not so sure. They studied all the problems and finally ordered that forty tanks be built. Swinton was again disappointed. He had hoped that hundreds would be built. Swinton's marvelous grin and his common sense helped win friends for the tank. The War Office increased the order to one hundred.

But the problems were only beginning. Tank crews had to be selected and trained. They had to learn how to service the armored monster, how to drive it, how to ride in it, and how to fire its gun. The questions of fuel and ammunition storage aboard the tank and of placing more fuel and ammunition in the tank on the battlefield had to be solved. There were also the problems of keeping the manufacture a secret from spies and the press, and how to transport the tanks across the English Channel. One of the biggest arguments arose as to when the vehicles should be used.

Colonel Swinton argued that the tanks should not be used until there were hundreds of them on hand. He knew that the Germans would be surprised. He hoped the tanks might make the long-looked-forward-to breakthrough.

But when General Haig heard of the new invention, he wanted to use it at once. He was planning a third attack against the German trenches in the Somme area and he needed help for his foot soldiers. Forty-nine tanks were sent to him.

When the tanks were sent into battle, fifteen broke down before they were driven into action. Others broke down as soon as they moved into the fight. Only eighteen managed to get into the battle, and of these some stalled in shell holes or ground to a stop in No Man's Land.

But the Germans were surprised by the monsters. One tank captured a fortified village. Another took 300 prisoners. But there were not enough tanks on hand to take advantage of the surprise and to break through.

Observers realized that the tanks were invaluable on modern battlefields, but that they would have to be improved. They were far too slow and were big, easy targets.

In October, the rains stalled the Battle of the Somme, just as mechanical difficulties had stalled many of the forty-nine tanks. General Ludendorff predicted that the "Somme mud" would end the five-month battle, and he was right.

The losses were tremendous. The dead by nations totaled:

French	195,000
British	420,000
German	650,000

The loss of so many men led to exhaustion. There is no doubt that the loss of 195,000 Frenchmen at the Somme and the deaths of 334,000 at Verdun will be felt by France for centuries.

Some of the finest stock in England died in the Battle of the Somme, and the Germans lost large numbers of their best veteran officers and noncommissioned officers.

The Somme battlefield, roughly twenty miles by nine, was a huge slaughterhouse. Historians and others have asked, "Why did General Joffre select the Somme area for an attack? How could he expect a breakthrough? Did he not know that the Germans had been working on their defenses there for two years? Why did Haig approve the idea of the battle?"

The best answer is a sorry one: in the Somme area, the British and French armies were alongside each other. The idea was that they should go forward shoulder-to-shoulder.

The battle ended in an atmosphere of gloom. The Allies captured about 190 square miles. All this amounted to was pushing the German lines back. There was no breakthrough. Nor did the Battle of the Somme pull Germans away from Verdun.

During the Battle of the Somme, a daring young messenger of a Bavarian regiment was wounded. His name was Adolf Hitler. He was a shrewd, fanatical fellow. When he became Chancellor of the Germans seventeen years later, he led his government on a path of terror and savage butchery unequaled in history.

When the terrible casualty lists from the Battle of the Somme were published in Britain, people were horrified. There were twenty-three men in the British War Cabinet. Placards, printed by an English newspaper, appeared on the streets bearing the words in heavy, black print: WANTED: 23 ROPES.

People of the Allied nations counted their losses. They asked themselves, "Can we go on?"

Chapter 14

WAR AT SEA

THE sailor who built the German fleet, Admiral von Tirpitz, did not want the Kaiser to declare war in the first place, but after the war started the old admiral wanted the German High Sea Fleet to fight. He saw no sense in the fleet's rusting in its harbors. The old sea dog felt that the blood of the German seamen must be spilled "gloriously" if Germany was to sink the English fleet.

The British Grand Fleet was the stronger of the two, and its admirals were well aware that the English people could afford no defeat at sea. The trade and food supply of the British Isles were dependent on the British fleet's ruling the oceans.

The two fleets lined up in strength like this:

BRITISH GRAND FLEET	GERMAN HIGH SEA FLEET
37 battleships and battle cruisers	27 battleships and battle cruisers
26 light cruisers	11 light cruisers
80 destroyers	63 destroyers
8 armored cruisers	

The admiral of the British Fleet, Sir John Jellicoe, was determined to avoid having *part* of his fleet battle the German High Sea Fleet. He also had his mind made up not to be drawn into a trap where he would lose warships by mines and submarines. Sir John was a kindly-looking man. He moved confidently about his flagship, the *Iron Duke,* but he carried a tremendous burden.

Winston Churchill phrased it when he said, "Jellicoe is the only man on either side who could lose the war in an afternoon."

The commander of the German High Sea Fleet, Admiral von Scheer, was a fighter. Not only was he naturally aggressive, but he felt the pressure of the German people, who wanted their navy to break the British blockade.

The crafty German raided the English east coast, hoping that Sir John Jellicoe would try to stop him by breaking the British fleet into small units. The German also expected to sink British warships with mines and submarines. Bad weather fouled Admiral Scheer's plans, and his submarines used up their supplies and had to come back. But Scheer did not give up. He knew that the British Grand Fleet sailed the North Sea every so often, so he decided to send out his scouting forces as a decoy. Perhaps he could catch the British fleet.

There were five German battle cruisers off Jutland as "bait" when the sea battle began, and, ready to rush into the battle area when they received the signal, were the fast German battleships. They expected to make their kill and get away. The date was May 31, 1916.

The British Admiralty in London had an ace—the German secret code—and was able to warn Jellicoe of the German plans.

Jellicoe put to sea with his main fleet. He sent Admiral Beatty with six battle cruisers to the "battle area." In midafternoon a young midshipman, high in the foretop of one of the battle cruisers, sighted five German cruisers, and the British opened fire. The range was ten miles. Immense columns of water marked the splashes of the projectiles. The destroyers on both sides scurried about to protect the larger ships from submarines. They were "black as cockroaches on a floor," one sailor wrote.

The Germans were better marksmen. The British battle cruisers *Invincible, Indefatigable,* and *Queen Mary* were hit hard. They blew up and sank, because the powerful projectiles exploited a fault in the ship's method of handling powder. The three cruisers slid under the waves carrying their crews to the bottom. Rear Admiral Hood went down on the *Invincible.*

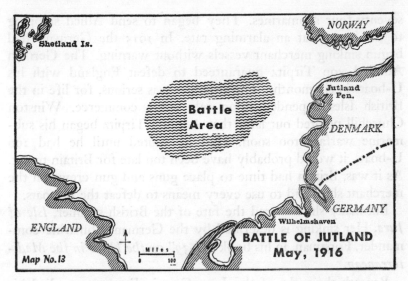

NORWAY

Shetland Is.

Battle Area

Jutland Pen.

DENMARK

GERMANY

ENGLAND

Wilhelmshaven

BATTLE OF JUTLAND
May, 1916

Map No. 13

Miles
0   100

Later, the main fleets clashed. Scheer hoped that the British would divide their fleet, but when he saw that they would not he broke off the fight and escaped with most of his fleet to his base at Wilhelmshaven. The British cruisers tried to get between the German warships and their base, but failed.

The German admiral was happy. He claimed victory because he sank British warships totaling 113,000 tons, while he lost 61,000 tons.

The Battle of Jutland was not a German victory; their fleet had to run for its base. Neither was it a victory for the British. Many Englishmen were disappointed in Sir John Jellicoe because he had not carried out the daring traditions of the British sea fighters. His countrymen thought him too cautious, but he had reason to be.

With their fleet bottled up for the war, the Germans depended upon their submarines, the U-boats. They believed this weapon would defeat England.

At the beginning of the war the Germans had twenty-seven subs. They worked feverishly to build more, but it took two years to build a U-boat. Nevertheless, by 1916 the Germans had seventy-four submarines. They began to send Allied shipping to the bottom at an alarming rate. In 1915 the Germans had begun sinking merchant vessels without warning. The German Admiral von Tirpitz guaranteed to defeat England with his U-boats in six months. The situation was serious, for life in the British Isles depended upon salt water commerce. Winston Churchill pointed out later that Admiral Tirpitz began his submarine warfare too soon. Had he waited until he had 200 U-boats, it would probably have been too late for Britain to act. As it was, Britain had time to place guns and gun crews on the merchant ships and to use every means to defeat the U-boats.

But many ships shared the fate of the British steamer, *Isle of Jura*. Her sinking is described by the German submarine commander, Forstman, in his book *"U-39" on the Hunt in the Mediterranean*.

Beneath the wake of the *Jura*, Captain Forstman studied his prey through the periscope. The *Jura* was zigzagging and running for all she was worth. Forstman realized that lookouts on the steamer had discovered his U-39.

The U-boat surfaced. Water poured through the scuppers. Captain Forstman gave an order and his gun crew, led by the cook, climbed up the conning tower, ran onto the slippery deck, and readied the gun. Lieutenant Donitz, gun commander, squinted into a blood-red sunset. The *Jura* appeared as if in a haze.

Donitz gave the commands. "Range 700. Left ten. High explosive. Two rounds." When the gun was ready, he screamed, "Fire!"

A column of water two hundred feet high shot into the air in front of the *Jura*. The next shot made a geyser under the stern. "Fire for effect!" shouted Donitz. Four shells pounded the steamer. One severed the cables to the rudder, and the wounded ship began to carve a circle in the sea.

Captain Forstman sent Lieutenant Donitz to the *Jura* in a canvas boat. Donitz found five of the *Jura's* crew badly wounded.

He saluted the British captain. "I am sorry, Mister Captain," Donitz said. "We have no doctor. I want your manifest papers and sailing orders. Prepare to abandon ship. Fast!"

There was no chance of escape from the sharklike U-39. The submarine lay 200 yards away, torpedos and gun trained on the steamer.

On the way back to the submarine, Donitz studied the *Jura*'s papers. "Ump-umph," he mused. "She has aboard 15,000 rounds of high explosive ammunition from Boston for our enemies in Genoa."

Shortly, Captain Forstman ordered two shots fired at the *Jura*'s waterline. The steamer listed to starboard, and in forty minutes stood on her stern and disappeared.

Before Captain Forstman submerged his sub to wait for another ship, he took a last look through the periscope at the eight lifeboats. In the fading light, the little boats looked like chips riding the waves. "They have one hundred and ten miles to Genoa," he said to his lieutenant. Then Forstman wrote up the death of the *Jura* in his log. Only by controlling his emotions could he keep from writing, "A very lonely, desolate scene."

To deceive the German submarines, ocean-going ships were painted the color of the mist. They were striped with odd designs, too, so that when submarine captains tried to sight them it was hard to tell the speed and exact direction of the ships. Destroyers worked hard to convoy groups of merchant vessels safely past the subs. Guns on some commercial ships were disguised by "cabins" which were built on their decks. When a submarine was sighted, part of the merchant crew acted as though in panic. They streaked for the lifeboats or ran up and down the decks. When the submarine surfaced to sink the vessel by gunfire, thereby saving a torpedo, the "cabin" about the merchant's gun collapsed and well-aimed shots poured into the raiding submarine.

Even with every safeguard inventive minds could think up, ships and their crews continued to be lost. Owners of neutral shipping were furious. The United States protested to the Kaiser.

So did other countries. But the Germans ordered their submarine captains to continue. "Lift the hunger blockade against our ports," German newspapers said, "and we will call in our submarines."

One mysterious sinking occurred near the Orkney Islands at the northern tip of Scotland. On board H.M.S. *Hampshire* was Lord Kitchener, en route to Russia to confer with the Czar and his top military leaders. "Lord K" was worried for fear Russia might collapse. If she did it would ease the pressure on Germany, and more German soldiers would be available to fight the Allies on the Western Front.

The cruiser *Hampshire* was steaming north when a powerful explosion shook her. The ship probably hit a mine laid by a submarine. The vessel quickly took on a fearful list. The alarm clanged to abandon ship. Eye-witnesses told later of the rush to get life rafts and lifeboats into the rough water and how "Lord K" calmly watched the feverish work. Men at a lifeboat that was ready shouted, "Make way for Lord Kitchener!" but the old general did not come. Wrapped in his great coat, he climbed a ladder to the quarterdeck. The captain called him, but he seemed not to hear. The ship plunged to the bottom fifteen minutes after it was struck. Lord Kitchener was never seen again.

Kitchener was not the great figure he had been at the start of the war in 1914, because he was blamed for the shortage of munitions, but most Englishmen grieved over his death. He was idolized by those who remembered the many years he had served England.

Perhaps the submarine threat to the lifeline of the British people was exaggerated. The Germans themselves suffered as a result of their ruthless, unrestricted U-boat warfare, because public opinion in the world's greatest neutral country, the United States, was inflamed against Germany. Lloyd George, the British prime minister, wrote, ... *The worst German blunder in the war was the quarrel with America.*

Most Americans still cared little about the war. They understood nothing about it. They were alarmed over the sinking of the world's largest ocean liner *Lusitania* by a U-boat in 1915, but they soon continued to concentrate on their daily business.

However, one American leader saw the world situation clearly —ex-President Theodore Roosevelt. From his home at Oyster Bay on Long Island, New York, "Teddy" Roosevelt tried his best to make Americans see that they would become involved. President Wilson was determined that the country remain neutral. He thought that his words and notes could stay the German force. But Roosevelt saw there was no escape from American entrance in the fighting, and he did his best to awaken Americans to their future.

Soon after the sinking of the *Lusitania*, fifteen American businessmen sent President Wilson a telegram. They, too, realized that the country was drifting toward war, and they also knew that the United States was unprepared. "Businessmen's Camps" were opened at Plattsburg, on Lake Champlain, New York. Thousands of American patriots attended the Plattsburg camps. They donned ill-fitting uniforms, quaint canvas leggings, wide-brimmed "campaign hats," and drilled under Regular Army sergeants and officers. President Wilson did not favor the Plattsburg camps, but they proved valuable. They helped train some of the American lieutenants and captains who were badly needed later.

But before the U-boat warfare drove the United States into the war on the side of the Allies, amazing battles and stupendous events occurred.

Chapter 15

GENERAL BRUSILOV WINS—
BUT RUSSIA LOSES

W HEN the Germans hurled hundreds of thousands of soldiers
against Verdun, the French sent the Czar a desperate plea:
*Please help us. If you will attack at once you will take the pres-
sure off Verdun.* The Italians were also hard-pressed. They, too,
begged the Czar to attack in order to draw Austrian soldiers
away from their attack on Italy.

As a result, for five days in March, 1916, Russian soldiers
attacked the Germans over the snows and in the mud near Lake
Narotch in northeastern Poland. Approximately 70,000 Russians
gave their lives.

Their victory made the Germans overconfident. One reason
they believed they could win, in spite of the Russian mud and
immense distances, was the behavior under fire of the German
soldiers. They were splendid.

One, a private, even turned the tide of battle when it seemed
that his company would be slaughtered. He was a quiet man, a
member of German Infantry Regiment Number 41. Until this
incident, Private Polotzek was a mousy fellow and colorless; a
man who always did things in a routine manner. Polotzek's main
enemy seemed to be his pack. The shoulder straps bit into his
shoulders. On the march his pack seemed to be the biggest in
the 9th Company of the regiment.

The morale of the 9th Company was low. The company had
advanced as close as it could to a grim Russian fortress, near Lake

Narotch, that dominated the countryside because it sat on a high hill. Private Polotzek, standing beside his pack in the forward trench of the company, overheard a gloomy conversation between his captain and his lieutenant.

The captain said, "We attack tomorrow. I never saw a fort in a better position." He shook his head. "I wrote my wife. It may be my last letter, for I do not see how we can win."

"If we knew where their machine guns were," the lieutenant said, "we might have a chance. We cannot attack at night. They place men out on the slope to listen."

After the two officers walked back along a trench leading to the rear, Polotzek raised his head cautiously. No shot came from the fort. This was the first time anyone in the 9th Company had been able to stick his head up over the forward trench without drawing fire. Polotzek wondered why the Russians had not fired. He did not know it, but the Russians thought their fort was so staunch that they had the Germans stopped. Private Polotzek looked over the ground toward the hill. It was one hundred yards to its base, another five hundred up the slope to the ramparts of the fort.

For reasons known only to himself, Polotzek stood on his pack and eased himself up on the top of the trench. He lay flat. No rifle shot came. He prayed that the Russians would not see him.

Before anyone could pull him back to safety, Polotzek squirmed like a lizard to a bush ten yards in front of the trench. The soldiers of the 9th Company were excited. They raised their heads cautiously. Some called to Polotzek, "Come back, you fool! You have no chance! You'll be killed!" But the small German paid no attention.

Polotzek looked like a gray spider as he inched his way uphill toward the Russian stronghold. He hid himself in every fold of the ground as he crawled to the top.

It took Polotzek an hour to reach the crest. The excitement in the trenches of the 41st Regiment was terrific. The Germans held their breath as Polotzek crawled carefully along the top of the hill a few yards from the Russian trench. Any minute the German soldiers below expected to see Polotzek killed.

After spending an hour spying on the Russians, Private Polotzek inched his way down the slope to his company. When he tumbled into the trench, the officers and noncommissioned officers clustered about him. Polotzek's uniform was shredded. There were scratches on his stomach and chest. "Tell us what you saw," the captain said.

"May I sit down, Herr Hauptmann—Mister Captain?"

"Please do."

Polotzek slumped downward in the trench and sat on his pack. The captain took notes as the little private talked.

"Two heavy machine guns with crews, they have up there in their trench," Polotzek said.

The captain frowned. He knew that when the attack started the machine guns would sweep the slope. The hill would be covered with dead Germans.

"Give me three volunteers, Herr Hauptmann," Polotzek said, "and in the morning we will crawl up the slope. We can bomb those guns and their crews."

The next morning, three hours after daybreak, the soldiers of the regiment watched Polotzek and his three men crawl into position a few yards from the Russians.

Polotzek raised his hand as a signal. Then he and his helpers threw high explosive bombs into the Russian trench. There was a roar. Earth sprayed over the four "bombers." The explosion was a signal for the regiment to leap out of its trenches. Only a few shots were fired from the fort as the Germans hurried to the top. The surprise attack, led by Private Polotzek, captured the fort.

After the fight, Polotzek's captain saluted him. "Polotzek," the captain said, "I am recommending you to our division commander, General Bothmer, for the Iron Cross, First Class. Is there anything else I can do for you?"

"*Ja*, Herr Hauptmann," Polotzek said, "have someone bring up my pack."

Polotzek received his pack and the Iron Cross, and was promoted to corporal two weeks later.

Over on the Russian side, the Czar appointed a new commander, a courageous, confident cavalryman: General Brusilov. Brusilov was a studious-looking fellow, fearless and smart. He believed he could win over the Austrians and Germans by attacking on a wide front. He discovered that in the past, when the Russians concentrated for an attack, spies alerted the enemy. "Therefore," General Brusilov told the leaders of his soldiers, "we will not concentrate for the fight."

So the Russian prepared to attack the Austrians on a 200-mile front. Brusilov was disappointed because he could not persuade other Russian generals also to attack. But he was undaunted. "I will attack alone with my army," he said.

The Russian general's dedicated work and courage paid. His army moved forward on the long front and broke the Austrian line in two places. Germany now had to go to the aid of the Austrians.

At this time Brusilov was hampered by the primitive transportation system of the Russians, while the Germans and Austrians, who had the advantage of a net of railroads, were able to concentrate men and guns faster at critical points.[1] By the end of the summer Brusilov's army was stopped. But he had accomplished much. He had helped the Italians, and he had forced the Germans to take soldiers away from the attack on Verdun. His success influenced Rumania to join the Allies, and he battered the Austrians.

However, Brusilov's desperate attack lost over 1,000,000 men. This great loss, coupled with the inefficient and heartless rule of the Czar, set the stage for revolution in Russia.

[1] See Map No. 7, page 54.

Chapter 16

RUMANIA BLUNDERS

SINCE the beginning of the war, the country of Rumania had been wondering how it could benefit from the fighting.[1] The war was all about them. It seemed to the Rumanians that all they had to do to gain was to join the winning side. The problem was how to determine which side was going to win. Bulgaria, another Balkan country, had also wondered on which side she could gain the most.

At first things looked fine for the Central Powers, when the Germans smashed through Belgium and wheeled on into France. But the fortress of Verdun held. The Rumanians bargained with the Allies for territory and plunged into the war on the Allied side.

The stern German General Falkenhayn had watched Rumania's fence-straddling, and he looked ahead. It appeared to him that Rumania would choose the Allied side, so he placed his hard fighter, Mackensen, and an army in Bulgaria. The German commander in chief ordered General Mackensen to draw up plans to crush Rumania should she become an enemy.

Rumania thought she was in a good position. The rugged Transylvania Alps to the north of the small country seemed a fine barrier, and so did the Danube River to the south. But the Rumanian Army was not ready to do battle. It lacked artillery, planes, machine guns, and rifles, and its transportation was primitive. Its senior officers were unskilled. The Rumanian leaders

[1] See Map No. 1, page 15, and Map No. 7, page 54.

saw the situation through a rosy cloud. The beautiful gains they thought they saw made them look forward to entering the war.

Late in August, 1916, Rumania made her plunge. Her armies drove through the passes of the Transylvania Alps to the north, headed into Austria. But soon the Rumanian Army slowed down, because its lack of training and equipment for mountain warfare acted as a brake.

Field Marshal von Mackensen, the small but fierce German leader, crossed the southern border with an army of Bulgarians, Turks, and a few Germans. Hard fighting started. At first the Rumanians were successful against Mackensen, but ammunition promised by the Allies failed to appear. Most of the ammunition had been sent, but it had to move through Russia, whose rail lines were in confusion.

Against the Rumanians in the north came General Falkenhayn, leading strong forces through the passes in the Alps. The Rumanians found themselves in a huge nutcracker. Under great pressure and desperate, they called on Russia for help.

The Russians had distrusted the Rumanians from the start, and disliked the Rumanian plan, but the Czar's soldiers tried to assist. The effort was not effective and the Germans took over most of the country. There was no formal surrender, but the Germans seized the Rumanian oil and wheat fields. The losses were 60,000 men for Germany and 350,000, perhaps more, for Rumania. The small country plunged into mourning.

While the Russians were trying to help the Rumanians, Cossacks and Russian soldiers from the Caucasus Mountains raided southern Galicia.[2] These were small raids. Russian tribesmen from the Caucasus Mountains were so wild they did not even know what a bureau drawer was for. When they attacked a village, they killed grandmothers, babies in arms, anyone. Sometimes their raiding parties were only three hundred strong, sometimes a thousand. The terror they aroused caused Rumanian refugees to pour southward. The Cossacks received pub-

[2] See Map No. 7, page 54.

Map No. 14

RUMANIAN COLLAPSE 1916

⇨ GERMANS, AUSTRIANS, TURKS, BULGARIANS
▲▲ RUMANIANS

Miles
0   20

AUSTRIA-HUNGARY

Gen. Falkenhayn

RUMANIA

Transylvanian Alps

○ Bucharest

Danube   River

BULGARIA

Gen. Mackensen

licity from the terrified Rumanians, and the myth grew that they were fierce fighters. Actually they did little except raid helpless civilians.

The Rumanian government made a severe error in declaring war when the Germans were ready to pounce on them. Equally bad was the decision of the Rumanian generals to plunge their armies northward when von Mackensen was in their rear. The loss of Rumania hurt the Allies, but a much greater tragedy was about to occur in Russia: a revolution. It would cost Czar Nicholas and his family their lives, and it has affected the course of the world ever since.

Chapter 17

THE RUSSIAN REVOLUTION

F EW Russian Czars were close to their people.
At the time of the American Civil War, Czar Alexander II
freed all of the Russian serfs—some 22,000,000—but his ideas of
helping the peasants gain land were clumsy. This created a
situation that led to revolution in 1917.

When political troubles arose in Russia, before the start of
the world war, the rulers blamed the Jews, and, as a result, there
were massacres. Then, in 1915, there were more dreadful events.
A priest led an angry crowd to the Czar's palace to present a
petition. Officers ordered the troops in front of the palace to
fire on the defenseless group. Strikes, riots, and killings followed.
This revolt gained the people liberties, but only for a short
time. Then the old, uncontrolled authority of the Czar began
all over again.

When the First World War started, the rule of Czar Nicholas
II was a government of highhandedness seasoned with weak-
ness. His people were downtrodden, his ruling class unconcerned
and arrogant. Neither Nicholas nor his nobles were interested in
improving the life of the peasants nor of the workers in the
factories. No one cared whether or not the common people
were able to make a living. The clergy were often ignorant.
Human life meant nothing unless it was the life of a noble.

When the war began, most Russians supported it. But the
amazing lack of interest in the people by the Czar and his nobles
was a cancer that could not be put aside. The rulers did not

recognize the great desire of the peasants to own land. Human beings were no more important to them than trash. The growing casualty lists and the shortage of food added to the despair of the people. The lack of interest in the people by the nobles made Russia ripe for revolution.

A dangerous situation existed, practically within the Czar's family. An evil monk, Rasputin, had a firm grip on the mind of the wife of the Czar, the Empress Alexandra. She was superstitious, and the ignorant monk controlled the Czar through her. The "holy man" could do no wrong, because he had cured her young son of a blood disease. Rasputin fixed his eyes, which blazed like lamps, on the Empress, and she did just as he said. His slightest whim became law. Rasputin was hated by the people, and, because the Czar and his wife were controlled by the monk, the people of Russia lost their respect for the royal family.

At the end of 1916 a group of Russian nobles decided that the way to save Russia was to murder Rasputin. They caused quantities of poison wine to be placed before him, which he drank with no ill effects. Next, they shot him, and he hardly showed the effects of the first bullets. The murderers had to riddle him with gunfire in order to kill him. Then, to make certain he was dead, they carried his body to a river and stuffed it under the ice.

But the death of the "holy man" only made the Czar harder. He became more superstitious and ruled with a steel rod. His people were even more miserable.

Rebellion broke out in St. Petersburg. The Czar fled from his throne and was later arrested. A revolutionist, Kerensky, who had liberal ideas, formed a government and carried on the war effort. But when news of the rebellion reached the front the morale of the soldiers dropped. Their food supplies were reduced.

Kerensky decided to make the army democratic, but this helped the rebellion to spread. Officers were murdered by their soldiers. Chaos developed. Kerensky's war effort failed and he was swept from power.

The Germans helped a revolutionist to step into this mess. Lenin, a middle-aged conspirator who looked harmless enough, with a sharp expression and a fringe of red hair bordering his bald head, was in exile in Switzerland. The Germans knew of the rebellion through their spies, and they also knew that if Lenin were back in Russia he would work to stop the war effort of the Russians and would try to start a civil war. So the Germans allowed Lenin to cross Germany en route to Russia in a railroad car. They sealed the car to make sure he got to Russia. They did not want Lenin loose in their country.

Lenin posed as a leader who would aid the Russians through kindly deeds, but his real power came from soldiers who carried out his orders. He spread the teachings of two Germans of the nineteenth century, Karl Marx and Friedrich Engels. They believed in class struggles. It was Marx and Engels who wrote, *Workers of the world, unite! You have nothing to lose but your chains.*

Marx's ideas caught on fast because Lenin pushed them. The Bolsheviks, who believed in taking political power by force, liked every thought Marx had written. So did other Russians who believed that destruction led the way to improvement. Terror spread. Political parties were outlawed. People who did not like the way things were running were lined up against a a wall and shot or were sent to slave camps in Siberia.

As soon as he felt he had the power, Lenin asked for an armistice with the Austrians and Germans. This was the last straw at the front. Russian soldiers broke away from the Germans and straggled home as best they could.

The end of the war on the Eastern Front was a blow to the Allies. It gave the Germans extra strength for the Western Front.

The surrender meeting took place at Brest-Litovsk, Russia, on the Bug River, and the Communist leaders expected easy terms. The Germans decided to make the Russians pay, and Lenin's right-hand man, Leon Trotsky, an amateur military man himself, argued bitterly. But Trotsky was up against a tough

German, General Max Hoffman. When Trotsky stalked angrily out of the conference, Hoffman merely gave an order and a German army started marching for St. Petersburg.

The Russians saw that they were powerless. They had to do exactly as the Germans said. They signed the treaty, now more harsh than at first. The Communists surrendered almost half a million square miles of land and 56,000,000 people to Germany. Germany and Austria received rich wheat lands, and grain was shipped westward at once.

The Russian leaders were downcast over the signing, but Lenin reminded them that long ago Russia had signed a treaty with Napoleon with the idea of breaking it as soon as possible. The Bolsheviks, cheered by this, were informed by the evil-planning Lenin that he would work to spread the Communist doctrine in all countries. He assured them that this would eventually enable them to rule the whole world.

Lenin was a dynamo of energy. Not only did he devote himself to world-wide Communism, but he worked with the Bolsheviks to enable them to bring all Russia under their power.

Chapter 18

THE UNITED STATES DECLARES WAR

M ost Americans were not concerned about the Russian revolution or the collapse of the Russian armies. Communism
seemed a faraway, weird revolutionist theory. And the war in
Europe had appeared to be remote until 1915, when a U-boat
sank the liner *Lusitania*.

Allied propaganda had been flooding the United States ever
since the invasion of Belgium. When the beautiful British nurse,
Edith Cavell, was executed by the Germans in Belgium for aiding
captured British soldiers, there was excitement. Millions of words
were written about her. Americans started to read about the
war in newspapers, magazines, and books. In their movie theaters,
newsreels devoted more and more footage to the fighting. The
Allies were featured, the Germans pictured in a bad light. There
was such an outpouring of atrocity stories that United States
news correspondents with the German armies protested.

Business in the United States skyrocketed. Ships carrying
munitions, food, and war supplies to the Allies made many
merchants wealthy. The British fleet prevented trade with Germany and Austria, but few minded because fortunes could be
made by trading with the Allies.

But when the U-boats sent trade ships to the bottom, public
opinion in the United States turned sharply against Germany.
Some United States citizens began to look closely at their Armed
Forces. The American Army was small. It had not covered
itself with glory in Mexico, when it chased the bandit, Villa.

The people of the United States discovered with a shock that their country was not ready for war. Preparedness parades were held in many cities by citizens who hoped their enthusiasm would cause the government to strengthen the Army and Navy.

Americans wondered about the use of airplanes in war. Planes were appearing more frequently in American skies. One man, who called himself "Diavolo," demonstrated wing-walking at fairs while the plane was in flight. Everyone read of the young aviators in the great war. People talked of Baron von Richthofen ("The Red Knight") who, before he died in combat, shot down single-handed eighty Allied planes. There was also the handsome Captain René Fonck of France, nicknamed "The Ace of Aces," who became the highest scoring Allied pilot, with seventy-five air victories. Britons were proud of "Mick" Mannock who, before he went down in a flaming plane, had seventy-three planes to his credit. Captain Albert Ball, RFC, attacked five German planes by himself, shooting down three of them. Early in the war, the Russians had their own air hero, Staff Captain Alexander Kazakov. This superstitious flyer would not take off unless he had his favorite icon, a tiny religious figure, in his cockpit. He tried to snag enemy planes with an anchor suspended beneath his plane. Captain Billy Bishop, of Canada, flew into the headlines when he shot down three German planes in a week and, a few days later, downed a German scout plane and an observation balloon. Americans wondered about their own aviators. People asked, "How many planes and aviators do we have?"

While no nation had a large air force, the air force of the United States (part of the Army Signal Corps) was puny. In early 1917 the United States had only thirty-five pilots and fifty-five planes. None of these planes were up-to-date combat types. To help get rid of old, obsolete planes, young Captain Henry "Hap" Arnold, a blond husky from Pennsylvania, took planes up and, when he brought them down, acted as though they were out of control. He taxied between two hangars, tearing off the wings. This was Arnold's dangerous way of readying the United

States for war. In World War II, Henry Arnold became a General of the Air Force and the United States aviation leader.

While the United States Navy was the third largest navy in the world, it was not prepared. It lacked officers and men. Its gunners needed battle practice. It had no aircraft and its submarines were antiques. The sinking of the submarine F-4 at her dock in Hawaii in 1915 seemed to typify the slothfulness gripping the United States Navy.

Pacifists in the United States were not interested in American preparedness, and they held their own parades, emphasizing peace. Their motto, "Peace at any price," was a far cry from Patrick Henry's creed, and it was scorned by most Americans. United States citizens with idealistic intentions backed Henry Ford when he sent a "peace ship" to Europe. Aboard were Americans who were determined to stop the war somehow, but the "peace ship" and its passengers accomplished nothing.

In 1917 the Germans believed they must stop the flow of war supplies from the United States to the Allies. It would be effective, the Germans thought, if they could cut off shipments of food to England. So on January 31 the Germans announced that they would sink, without warning, all sea traffic bound for Allied ports. The Germans said they did not care whether the ships were from a neutral country or not. This was against the rules of international conduct, but the Germans pointed out that they were only using their submarines to accomplish the same results that the British had with their surface fleet.

Many United States citizens believed that their ships should stay out of the war zones, but trade was too lucrative. Ships flying the Stars and Stripes sailed for Europe and were sent to the bottom in large numbers.

A French war mission, headed by the famous Papa Joffre, visited the United States. War fever swept the country. President Wilson said, "We have no selfish ends to serve, we desire no conquest. . . . We are but one of the champions of mankind." The President knew how to make the aims of the United States sound noble.

One night, at Black Tom, part of Jersey City, New Jersey, men working for the Kaiser blew up an ammunition plant. The loss of property was heavy.

More merchant ships plunged to the bottom. On April 6, 1917, at a special session called by President Wilson, Congress declared war against Germany. This was no "War of 1812 Declaration," when a majority of only six votes placed the country in a war. The Senate voted 82 to 6 for war; the House 375 to 50. Excitement gripped every American home, farm, factory, village, town, and city. Differences in opinion were dropped in many areas; people listened, and began to understand each other. A great American Crusade started.

There were rumors of spies and sabotage. People avoided German restaurants and shops. Ministers in their pulpits lashed out at the "Huns." Recruiting offices were swamped by volunteers rushing to enlist. The word "slacker" was coined for persons unwilling to serve their country. Pacifists and conscientious objectors (people who said it was against their religion or their consciences to fight) were treated roughly.

Enthusiasm sometimes went to foolish extremes. Sauerkraut was renamed "Liberty Cabbage." Dachshunds were stoned. Boys named "Fritz" demanded that their parents change their names. Civil War veterans led parades, carrying signs: CALL ON US IF THE BOYS CAN'T DO IT. WE ARE READY TO GO. Even the President marched at the head of a parade carrying a flag. Bands played "The Star-Spangled Banner" in the streets, and if you failed to remove your hat it was in danger of being knocked off. The Stars and Stripes flew over the Houses of Parliament in London, the first time any foreign flag had been hoisted there. Americans started "Liberty Gardens," growing their own food so that more would be available for the Armed Forces. Many schools stopped teaching German, and some libraries burned German books. There were rumors of German intrigue with Mexico.

French and British war heroes, many of them wounded, toured the United States to help sell United States defense bonds in the

The New York Times.

"All the News That's Fit to Print."

THE WEATHER

VOL. LXVI...NO. 21,623.   NEW YORK, SATURDAY, APRIL 7, 1917.—EIGHTEEN PAGES.

PRESIDENT PROCLAIMS WAR; WARNS ALIEN ENEMIES HERE; 91 GERMAN SHIPS SEIZED AND SPIES PUT UNDER ARREST; NAVY MOBILIZED AT ONCE; CUBA AND BRAZIL 'MAY JOIN US

27 SHIPS TAKEN HERE

Government May Use Liners Later as Troop Transports.

VATERLAND NOT DAMAGED

Soldiers Aid Collector Malone in Removing 1,100 Officers and Men to Ellis Island.

TOOK SEIZURE STOICALLY

Sang and Cheered as They Left Pier—Women and Children, Detained, May Be Released.

MEXICAN DEMANDS WAR

President Urges Congress to Authorize Action; No Opposition Expected.

VOTE WILL BE TAKEN TODAY

Executive Emphasizes German Lawlessness and Cuba's Duty to Stand by Us.

BRAZIL EXPECTS A BREAK

Sinking of Steamship Parana Likely to Cause Rupture with Berlin.

Think German Kaiser Vetoed Peace Proposal by Austria

SPIRIT OF REFORM RIFE IN GERMANY

Vorwaerts Voices Demand for Sweeping Changes and Abandonment of Idea of Conquest.

WAR'S FAILURE REALIZED

Entry of America Into the Conflict Believed to Have Had a Powerful Effort.

WHOLESALE PLOT ARRESTS

Sixty German Suspects in New York and Other Cities Locked Up.

ACT PASSED IN 1798 INVOKED

As on the War of 1812, Seizures Are Made Without Reference to Courts.

THIRTEEN ARE HELD HERE

Paul Koenig One of the First Taken—Police Hunt Weapons.

President's Proclamation of a State of War, and Regulations Governing Alien Enemies

WASHINGTON, April 6.—The President's proclamation to the American people announcing the existence of a state of war is as follows:

A PROCLAMATION.

GOVERNMENT ACTS SWIFTLY

War Tidings Fly to Navy and Army When Wilson Signs Resolution.

CABINET IN LONG SESSION

Co-operation with Entente a Leading Theme—Other Big Problems Under Discussion.

WORLD TOLD OF ACTION

Proclamation by the President Fixes Aliens' Bounds—and Summons Citizens to Aid.

Bryan Asks the President to Enroll Him as a Private

TALLAHASSEE, Fla., April 6.

BRITISH PREMIER PRAISES WILSON

Lloyd George Says America Has Become a World Power In a New Sense.

CAUSE WORTHY OF NATION

Statement Issued for the War Cabinet Singles Out Three Praises in Wilson's Address.

famous "Liberty Loan" drives, which raised the money to finance the war. Detachments of crack French mountain fighters, "The Blue Devils," paraded in American cities to stirring bugles and drums. United States troops marching with them, and small boys tagging alongside were unable to keep up with the Frenchmen's swift, running walk. Newspapers hailed the visitors and devoted as much space as possible to the war.

The details of the sinking of more ships spurred the United States. Loss of trade, ships, and lives brought indignation in the United States to a white heat. The national honor seemed at stake. It was obvious that if shipping losses were not sharply reduced, and in a hurry, the Allies would lose the war.

Germany's ruthless submarine warfare was one of the greatest mistakes in all history. But the Germans were not aware of it until after the war. They were confident. By early 1917, trainloads of victorious German soldiers were arriving in France from the Eastern Front, and German submariners were dauntless at sea. One German admiral announced, "The war effort of the United States will amount to zero."

The Allies prayed for American help, and that it would arrive quickly.

Chapter 19

TWO AMERICAN LEADERS
GO "OVER THERE"

BEFORE United States soldiers could take their places in the trenches with the allies, much work lay before them. The task was gigantic because the country was so unprepared. The Army of the United States especially needed attention. It would have to be greatly expanded, trained, disciplined, equipped, transported across the Atlantic, and supported. Time was the taskmaster lashing Americans.

It soon became obvious that the country could not build up its Armed Forces just by swearing in volunteers. Major General Leonard Wood had an idea. "Let's have a draft," he said. Secretary of War Newton Baker saw that the idea was smart, and he pushed it. Congress approved.

Twenty-four million Americans registered for the draft. Ten million between the ages of twenty-one and thirty-five had numbers assigned them. In the first drawing, Mr. Baker stood blindfolded in front of a goldfish bowl filled with capsules, each of which contained a slip of paper on which was written one of those numbers. He drew the first number, 258. It had been assigned to a man in Mississippi, who sent Mr. Baker a telegram: *Thank you for drawing me.* The goldfish bowl was filled again and again. The drawing went on for sixteen and one-half hours, until 1,374,00 names were selected.

Physical examinations weeded out the unfit. Before the men

who were to serve could report, camps (or "cantonments") had to be built. Thirty-two were constructed—a gigantic task.

Supply depots had to be constructed in France, and stocked with ammunition, food, clothing, mules, harness, trucks, and so on. Hospitals had to be built to take care of the wounded.

Orders were placed for uniforms and supplies. Since we had no modern artillery, we arranged to buy the famous "French 75," and other cannons. We also had to buy airplanes from the French.

Many more officers and noncommissioned officers had to be selected and trained. Leaders had to learn about weapons, tactics, and how to take care of their men. The best enlisted men of the Regular Army were a source for leaders. So were young men in the colleges and universities who were in the Reserve Officers Training Corps.

Cadets were graduated early at the United States Military Academy at West Point so that they could serve their country sooner. By November 1918 the Corps of Cadets consisted of only one class, the Plebes.

Groups from civilian life who were eligible for officers' commissions were sent to camps where they trained hard under Regular Army officers for ninety days. "Ninety-day wonders," they called themselves. These men became devoted, efficient officers. It was largely the "Ninety-day wonders" who led Americans "over the top" in 1918.

At Gettysburg, Pennsylvania, a young captain from Kansas was training men for the newly formed Tank Corps. His name was Dwight Eisenhower. In World War II he rose to five-star rank and later became President.

When young Cadet Eisenhower was a halfback on the Army football team at West Point, one of his teammates was a boy from Missouri, Omar Bradley. Bradley also became a General of the Army in the Second World War. In World War I, Eisenhower and Bradley were not in the spotlight. They had the hard, backstage job of training soldiers. Another future famous leader had the even less glamorous task of teaching West Point cadets the French language. This was a boy born in Virginia, Matthew B. Ridgway. In battles of the Second World War and in the Korean War he was fearless and dynamic, wearing general's stars.

To lead the huge army that was training so hard, President Wilson selected a leader, John J. Pershing, a Missourian. Pershing was a severe, dedicated worker, a stern man who knew the value of discipline.

John Pershing had a long military background. At West Point he was first captain in the Corps of Cadets. Later he fought Apaches on the Western Plains. At San Juan Hill in 1898 he earned the Silver Star medal for bravery. He battled the Moros in the Philippines. He commanded the American soldiers on the Mexican border against the bandit, Pancho Villa. Pershing was experienced. He had an odd nickname, "Black Jack," given him because he had once commanded Negro troops. "Black Jack" seemed to match his mood at times. Pershing had great courage. When he became the commanding general of the American Expeditionary Force, everything seemed against him, but he plunged into the task with energy. He demanded the utmost from people under him.

Before General Pershing sailed for Europe, Secretary of War Baker decided that the A.E.F. was to be a separate army. Mr. Baker believed that American soldiers would fight better as a unit under the Stars and Stripes than if placed in small groups under the Tricolor of France or the British Union Jack.

As soon as he could, Pershing and his staff sailed for London and Paris. The military-looking, military-acting general was received with great enthusiasm. He was taken to the tomb of Lafayette, champion of the American cause in 1776. In the crowd before the speaker's stand stood French veterans headed by Joffre. General Pershing made a speech, but a member of his staff, Colonel Charles Stanton, spoke words which thrilled Frenchmen when he said, "Lafayette, we are here."

To command the United States Navy, the President chose Vice Admiral William Sims, an officer with a fine naval record.

Sims sailed at once for England, where he met his friend, Sir John Jellicoe, of the British Navy. Sims quickly learned that the situation was far more serious than Americans realized. "It looks as though the Germans are winning," Admiral Sims said, and Jellicoe agreed. More and more U-boats were appearing, and British spies reported in 1917 that the Germans were building 400 more to reinforce their fleet of 111.

The answer, the two admirals believed, lay in sub-chasers, better destroyers, and more efficient depth bombs. The Germans were quick to counter these moves. They built sturdier submarines and, to discourage sub-chasers and destroyers from ramming them, they placed false periscopes on floating mines.

The entry of the United States into the war was hailed by the Allies, but soon Allied leaders asked General Pershing and Admiral Sims, *"Where is the United States Army?"* The Allies had their backs pressed against a wall. They needed help badly.

The old Regular Army had been a few thousand men—barely enough to handle Indians, bandits, and Moro tribesmen. Now millions of men were needed to face the veteran, victorious armies of Germany. The list of techniques soldiers had to learn seemed endless. Instructors with combat experience were needed, so the British and French sent eight hundred experienced officers of all ranks. The new United States Army plunged into its task with enthusiasm.

The soldiers trained long hours. At Camp Jackson, South Carolina, the soldiers developed an odd nickname for themselves. They started calling themselves "wildcats." The road from camp to Columbia was named Wildcat Road, and this struck their fancy. The nickname appealed to them because this fierce animal roamed the forests near their homes and because wildcats never avoided a fight.

One day some of the soldiers of the 81st Division at Camp Jackson fashioned small disks of cloth and cut out the centers to resemble a wildcat with its paw raised, about to strike. They asked their general, Charles J. Bailey, for permission to sew their emblems on the left shoulder of their uniforms, and the general said "Yes."

When men of the 81st went to Columbia the following Saturday, military police worked overtime stopping fist fights between the "wildcats" and soldiers of other divisions. A military police officer asked the men of the 81st why they were fighting and they answered, "Those other fellows made fun of our shoulder patches. They called the wildcat a 'woods-pussy,' and we're not standing for that."

Other generals said to themselves, "If soldiers of the 81st Division will fight for their insignia, let us have one."

Men of the 81st Division on their way to France asked to be allowed to adopt the wildcat shoulder insignia. The War Department approved, and the shoulder patch was born in the United States Army.

The problem of shipping 2,000,000 soldiers to France with their weapons, food, ammunition, and other equipment was gigantic. The Allies helped by sending ships. American shipyards worked overtime. Before "Liberty Ships" could be built, the shipyards had to be expanded, and temporary cities near the shipyards had to be built to house the workers. This was before the day of big fleets of cargo trucks, and a great burden was placed on the railroads. On the farms and in the factories, men and women labored hard so that our Army, Navy, and Marines could be made ready and so that they could win.

In Europe more and more pressure was placed on General Pershing by political and military leaders. "It will take too long to train the United States Army so it can fight as a separate unit," they said. "Let its men come over at once. We will place them in our armies as replacements for men who have been killed or wounded."

One of the most demanding, one of the most acid in his comments on the slowness of the American Army, was Georges Clemenceau, Premier of France. His nickname was "The Tiger." He had a saw-edged tongue and a mind like a rapier. Once, in an argument with a political enemy, Clemenceau lashed out,

"You are not God." "And you are not the devil," his enemy replied. "How do you know I'm not?" The Tiger snapped. M. Clemenceau said the Americans were slow, and by the time they learned to fight the war would be lost.

General Pershing explained that American soldiers were not to serve in a foreign army.

"Change the order," Clemenceau demanded. Other foreign political leaders backed him. "Never mind your guns," they said, "bring your men. We'll give them weapons. It is men we want. If we do not get them quickly we may lose the war."

The British commander, Field Marshal Sir Douglas Haig, who could be as stubborn as Pershing, pleaded with him, but Pershing remained firm. Lloyd George, the British Prime Minister, added his political force to the argument.

General Pershing refused to budge. He believed that the war was far from lost, and that the Americans would fight better under American leaders. He explained the pressure he was under in a cable to Mr. Baker.

Mr. Baker insisted that his order to General Pershing remain unaltered. Baker was certain it would work. "National pride is at stake," he said. President Wilson supported Baker's idea, to the tremendous disappointment of the Allies.

America buzzed with work. War music and war songs rang. George M. Cohan wrote a song, "Over There." Soldiers and sailors were buoyed by it. It pledged the United States' spirit and determination. Bands blared it. People sang:

> "Over there, over there,
> Send the word, send the word over there
> That the Yanks are coming, the Yanks are coming! ...
> And we won't come back till it's over over there."

But to the Allies holding the battle lines, things were not as gay as the song. The pace of the United States seemed slow as a snail's. The Allies would have to hold for thirteen more grueling months before United States soldiers could come into action in large numbers.

"The war to end war," "The war to make the world safe for Democracy," World War I, was undertaken by Americans with zeal and enthusiasm. Regular Army and Navy officers were anxious to fight in it. But they were the only trained officers available. Many of them had to be held in the United States to form new regiments.

Russell Reeder, Regular Army colonel from Cincinnati, Ohio, trained an artillery regiment. When he finally placed it aboard ship so it could travel to France, orders arrived for him to turn the regiment over to another officer and to train another regiment. Reeder carried out the order, but before the second regiment was ready to depart he telegraphed the War Department that if he had to train still another regiment he would resign. The War Department recognized his spirit, and he sailed with his second regiment of artillery for France.

While the United States Army readied itself for combat, Allied casualties mounted. The Allies continued to beg for American soldiers.

The Germans were also losing men. Food in Germany was scarce. But the Kaiser, living in a world of his own, was confident. He exaggerated the effect of his U-boat campaign when he said grandly, "My officers inform me they can scarcely find an enemy vessel on the high seas."

The war hung in the balance. French politicians demanded a new military leader. To them, Pape Joffre was not the hero he was in 1914. To men in the French government in 1916 who disliked him because of his undisputed rule and because of the way he controlled the press, Joffre was a relic. To replace Marshal Joffre, a charming young Frenchman, Robert Nivelle, was promoted over the heads of several famous French generals.

Nivelle explained his plans in an enchanting manner. His mother was an Englishwoman, and General Nivelle spoke flawless English. Lloyd George was so fascinated with the smooth-talking general that he proposed making Nivelle commander in chief of both the French and British armies. This angered the British generals. To make matters worse, Nivelle had another side to his character: he issued his orders in an abrupt manner. Many officers found him insulting.

Nivelle's rise to high command had been rapid. Political leaders were impressed with him, but British generals were not. The Germans were relieved when they heard that Papa Joffre had been retired. "That is a godsend," they said.

Robert Nivelle discussed his plans with almost anyone. In his mind, he was the man of the moment. He issued an order, "The hour has come! Confidence! Courage! *Vive la France!*" He also said, "The motto of every commander must be violence, brutality, and rapidity."

There were some who believed that General Nivelle was a bad choice. Some were swayed by his magnetism, but others wondered about his leadership.

Chapter 20

"ALL QUIET ON THE WESTERN FRONT"

IN 1917, while the British haggled with General Nivelle, existence in the trenches went on. Living in them was depressing; men with weak nerves could not stand it. Fighting in them was hard.

An example of trench warfare in France is described by the German Lieutenant Colonel Rommel in his book, *Infantry Attacks*.[1] Rommel, at the time of this incident, was a young second lieutenant. He had been wounded, but was back on duty. The Kaiser had presented him with the Iron Cross for bravery.

A rehearsal for the trench fight Rommel describes was held just as if it were a play. But instead of having the rehearsal on a stage, the soldiers were trained in a duplicate trench system far behind their lines. The troops went over their parts time and again until every man knew what he was to do. The idea would be to capture a part of a French trench by cutting it off.

The first part of the "play" was an artillery bombardment. German artillery punished the French trenches, in the vicinity of the trench that was to be captured, for three hours. This in itself was dangerous to the German infantry attackers, because the trench they were to capture was only forty to seventy yards away.

[1] Erwin Rommel became a famous German commander in World War II. In that war he commanded Hitler's Afrika Korps in the North African desert, and also the "West Wall" of Europe at the time of the Normandy Invasion (1944). Rommel was a brave, able leader.

135

Flying dirt and stones showered the Germans, who crouched against the forward wall of their own trench. An artillery shell that fell short of its aim killed two men. Lieutenant Rommel walked up and down the German trench to show his men he was unafraid and to see how they fared. The explosion of a shell knocked him down. Fortunately for him, he was not hit by any of the shell fragments. The crack of the cannonade was fearful. Rommel rose to his feet and brushed off his uniform. He felt anxious. The bombardment was necessary, but there was no room for error by German artillerymen. His men were nervous. The crack of the artillery and the showers of dirt and iron fragments bothered them. But they knew that the artillery fire was a necessary evil and would help them when they had to go over the top.

When the German artillery ceased firing at ten forty-five in the morning, 400 Germans climbed out of their front-line trench and sprinted across No Man's Land.

French infantry, "fear-crazed," Rommel called them, climbed out of their trench when they saw the Germans above them. The French held their hands high and surrendered. Rommel and his company continued to play their parts by running on to the next French trench. The idea was to prevent French soldiers in rear trenches from coming to the aid of men who had just been captured.

French machine-gunners in other trenches opened fire. Rommel's men threw themselves down and returned the fire. French infantry, in trenches farther back, counterattacked. The din was terrific. The French infantry coming to the rescue was stopped and part of their front lines became German.

Ammunition supply now became a problem for the 400 Germans. Rommel's major ordered a trench dug all the way back to the German front line so that ammunition could be carried forward. Rommel's men were ordered to return to the captured trench and to help dig. A sandbag wall had to be built in the captured trench as a shield against French machine-gun fire that was raking the position. Hours had raced by. Rommel and his soldiers were so excited they had forgotten to eat. It was now ten o'clock at night. Flares were shot up by both sides so that men in the trenches could see what was coming at them in No Man's Land. It was an eerie scene.

To build this sandbag wall was hell, Rommel wrote. He ordered his men to lie on their backs and to form an endless chain, passing the sandbags up all the way from the rear. Steel shields were also passed up to protect men building the sandbag wall. A friend of Rommel's, Lieutenant Stöwe, who had leave orders in his pocket, was killed. Eventually, Rommel's men dug more trenches to make the captured trench part of their system.

Trench warfare was bloody, unglamorous, dirty, depressing, and back-breaking work. Both sides conducted rehearsals and attacks like Rommel's. Sometimes thousands and thousands of men were engaged in the battles for enemy trenches.

On other occasions there might be little fighting in a locality for a week or longer. In times of inaction the soldiers were far from idle. Trenches had to be repaired, rain water pumped out of dugouts. Weapons and ammunition required cleaning. Food, water, mail, medicine, and ammunition had to be hand-carried to the front. Patrols went out nightly to discover what the enemy was up to.

Patrolling in No Man's Land at night was hard. It was not a job that was sought after. The greenish-white flares that arched into the sky made the blackness seem even darker. Every once in a while, automatic weapons roared. They cut red streaks of fire in the darkness. Men on patrol became separated. They fought hand-to-hand with enemy patrols or men in enemy trenches, or lay still for hours under nerve-racking conditions in order to gain information. Patrol leaders venturing into No Man's Land soon learned that they had traveled only half as far as they thought they had. Bringing a patrol back to its own lines was dangerous because, in the dark, it was easy to be mistaken for an enemy patrol.

Patrol fights, and even battalion fights like Rommel's, were seldom reported in the newspapers. Soldiers looking for an account of their action in home-town papers were often irritated to read: *All quiet on the Western Front.*

Things were "quiet" when the new Allied commander in chief, General Nivelle, explained his plan for victory. He said that it would end the war. The trouble was he explained his idea not only to Field Marshal Sir Douglas Haig and his staff, but to all who would listen. Nivelle loved to talk. He talked so much about his secret plan that it was even discussed back in London at a cocktail party. German spies sent it to the Kaiser's generals. In addition, copies of Nivelle's orders were captured. The men who were to pay were in the trenches. They knew nothing of this. They just kept things "quiet" and tried to survive.

The Germans now (February 25–April 5, 1917) moved back about twenty-five miles in central France. When General Nivelle heard of this he shrugged his shoulders and said, "It is of no concern."

But by withdrawing the Germans shortened their lines and saved manpower. They called their new position "the Siegfried Zone." The Allies termed it the Hindenburg Line.

The Hindenburg Line was not a single defensive line. It was a defensive zone from three to twenty-five miles wide—the strongest part of their long defensive system. The Hindenburg Line stretched from Arras and Valenciennes in northern France to a point on the Aisne River near Soissons.[2]

In this "line" the Germans fortified every house, hill, ravine, and canal. They laced the zone with miles of trenches. Trees were cut down so gunners and riflemen would have clear fields of fire. Barbed-wire entanglements were strung on iron stakes so Allied artillery could not shoot them down easily. The Germans were proud of their work. They believed the Siegfried Zone would stop any force, that it was the toughest defensive line the world had ever seen.

In order to reach the Hindenburg Line, the Allies had to advance over land the Germans had wrecked. The Germans had laid booby traps for the Allies, and even poisoned the wells.

[2] See Map No. 19, page 206.

General Nivelle readied his armies for a smash straight ahead, south of the Hindenburg Line. He hoped to make a gap with infantry, artillery, and tanks. He ordered large forces of cavalry to stand by. "Be ready to ride through the gap," he said.

General Nivelle's well-advertised "secret plan" hinged on Haig's British Army plunging across No Man's Land at Vimy and at Arras.[3] The French were to attack farther south. These were naked power plays. There was no surprise.

The British readied forty-eight of the new tanks.

Above this part of the battlefield the R.A.F. was in control. It was able to sweep the air because it had bombed German airfields just behind the battle lines.

At first, at the town of Arras, the British attack rolled fast. In clouds of snow flurries which hurt the aim of the defenders, the Canadians captured Vimy Ridge, a key point of the battlefield. No troops ever fought harder than the Canadians at Vimy Ridge. The Allied cavalry received its orders to attack, but it was so far back that by the time it arrived at the front its horses were exhausted. The forty-eight tanks were insufficient. The weather changed and the rains turned the chalky earth into a gluelike mud. Now the rain turned to snow and sleet. The tanks bogged down in the muddy shell holes. The British attack slowed up. This was April, 1917.

In May, shifting their attack to a point farther north near Ypres, the British bored tunnels under the German-held Messines Ridge.[4] The "Tommies" filled the underground corridors with 1,000,000 pounds of high explosive. When the powder exploded the ridge was wrecked, but another stalemate quickly developed. The Battle at Arras made only limited gains for the Allies. It cost the British 84,000 men.

For the French attack at the Aisne River, General Nivelle had chosen a difficult piece of ground. It was almost as if he dared his 1,200,000 soldiers to succeed. The plan called for a fight up wooded slopes and stark cliffs. Because of Nivelle's boasts, the

[3] See Map No. 19, page 206.
[4] See Map No. 19, page 206.

soldiers believed they would win easily. They dreamed of home and the end of the war.

The French attack started with everything wrong. French artillery pounded the German trenches, but April rain changed into snow, delaying the attack. When the Frenchmen did attack they soon became low on ammunition. Heavy packs weighed down the fighters and exhausted them. Confusion reigned.

The French air force was driven from the skies over the battle-field. At this time, Germany's ace, von Richthofen, was at his best. In one air battle a British pilot made a sieve of Richthofen's gasoline tank. The Baron landed his famous red triplane behind his lines, quickly secured another plane, and zoomed to the attack. In a short time he brought down a Royal Air Force D.H.2.

French tanks, waddling along in the attack, had cans of reserve gasoline strapped to them. Shell fragments piercing the cans set the gas on fire, and many tanks burned with their crews. The French infantry fought bravely, but it was able to go only two miles. The French took 21,000 prisoners, but for them and the two miles of German trenches, France paid by having 100,000 men killed or wounded.

The failure on the Aisne River seemed to be the end of everything to the French soldiers. Mutiny broke out. The French soldiers saw no hope. They could see only desolation and death. They were tired. Communists and agitators worked fast to increase the despair by spreading pamphlets and by talking treason. The French soldiers refused to obey their officers. General Nivelle lost the respect of his men. They would not carry out his orders. "We will go into the trenches," they said, "but we will not attack." Some units started to march on Paris to demand peace.

General Nivelle's glamor vanished. Even his booster, Lloyd George, saw that he was a failure as a high commander. Nivelle's command was taken from him and General Henri Pétain, a hero of Verdun, was given the task of restoring the spirit of the crumbling regiments.

Pétain went personally to the ranks and investigated the

troubles of the men. He visited ninety divisions. He weeded out the ringleaders of the mutiny. General Pétain found that some men had not been on leave for three years. He increased leaves, and saw that the food became better. Pétain used his personal magnetism to persuade noncommissioned officers and junior leaders to pull their units together and to fight again for France. Fortunately for the Allies, General Pétain stopped the mutiny before the Germans became aware of it. Pétain's leadership in this crisis saved France.

The mutiny in the French Army occurred just before General Pershing arrived in France. Allied leaders said, "Look at this trouble. We need to place your soldiers in French units."

But Pershing would not give in. The British and French shook their heads. They told him that his stubbornness would cost the Allies the war.

Pétain worried. He said to Haig and to leaders in the French government, "I hope the Americans will not arrive too late."

I N America, preparations hummed. General Pershing had sent word back that he wanted the number of men in the United States infantry division, our main striking force, increased to 28,000 men. This was about twice the size of a British or French division. Twenty-eight thousand men in one division was an unwieldy force, but Pershing figured that tremendous power was needed to crash through the German lines.

The United States Army had a wonderful rifle, the bolt action 1913 Springfield caliber .30, but it took too long to manufacture. To speed up arming American infantrymen, the British rifle was altered to fire U. S. Army ammunition. This was the Lee-Enfield rifle. And machine guns and automatic rifles were purchased from the British and the French for the first divisions to go overseas. Later, the Browning automatic rifle and Browning machine gun, both of American design, were given to the United States infantry. Great effort was placed behind the manufacture of the Liberty twelve-cylinder airplane engine, but on the whole America's effort to supply airplanes was unsuccessful. This was largely because the United States had to build almost its entire aircraft construction industry before it could start manufacturing planes.

One of the biggest problems the United States faced was transporting its army and supplies overseas. Two million men, their weapons, baggage, and supplies had to cross 3,000 miles of ocean. Ports, warehouses, roads, railroads, and signal communications

had to be built. It was a gigantic task. The leaders soon discovered that it was easier to transport soldiers than cargo. This was
because the planners did not foresee that certain supplies would
be needed before other supplies. The cargo was so mixed up that
General Pershing cabled the United States not to send any more
bookcases, bathtubs, office desks, floor wax, stepladders, lawn
mowers, refrigerators, settees, sickles, stools, and window shades.

General Pershing took one of his best officers, General James
Harbord, a soldier from Illinois, and gave him the task of clearing
cargo from the ports. "Straighten out the supply system,"
Pershing told Harbord. Harbord solved the problem chiefly by
bettering the morale of the workers and by making their work
competitive, racing one unit against another in moving supplies.
He called the contest, "The Race to Berlin." The work sped
faster.

To place the United States National Army (as it was called)
in France, all kinds of ships were used: battleships, ocean liners,
tramp steamers, and vessels seized from the Germans when war
was declared. Ships were painted a crazy-quilt pattern in order
to confuse submarine captains as to their direction and speed.

The U-boats were at their peak in April, 1917. In that month
they sank almost 1,000,000 tons of shipping. This was a crisis of
the war. Not only was the existence of Great Britain, which
needed food from overseas, at stake, but the Allies were worried
over the safety of the American Army on the ocean. Some Allied
leaders hesitated to admit it, but they needed the American Army
in order to win.

To defeat the submarines, ships were convoyed. That is, they
were sent across the Atlantic in groups protected by the United
States Navy and also by the Royal Navy. This smart idea cut
losses sharply. To sink ships, German submarines had to risk
being sent to the bottom, and many U-boats did go down.
Working against them with thousands of other United States
naval officers was Commander William F. Halsey, Jr. Halsey
served on two destroyers which were engaged in convoy duty,

and also against German submarines. His work in the face of danger earned him the Navy Cross.

Another winner of the Navy Cross, also a Naval Academy graduate, was Ernest J. King. This tall, severe-looking officer served in the Atlantic Fleet. Both leaders rose to the five-star rank of Fleet Admiral in World War II.

The Allied convoys were carefully protected. Another measure against the German submarines was a huge belt of 70,000 mines stretching from Scotland to Norway. This plan for penning up the submarines in the North Sea, it was hoped, would keep them out of Atlantic shipping lanes. The idea was not accepted at first by the British, but when more efficient submarine mines, mines anchored beneath the surface, were developed, the British accepted the plan. Our Navy laid 56,000 of these mines. It was hard, dangerous work. After the war it was discovered that this belt of mines had sent twelve U-boats to the bottom.

While our soldiers were crossing the Atlantic, news came to the United States of a great British effort at Ypres, in Flanders, Belgium. The French Army had not recovered completely from its mutiny. To gain time so that it could climb back on its feet, General Pétain begged Field Marshal Haig to have his army attack. Haig agreed to help. He drew up a plan by which he hoped to free the Belgians from their conquerors, and at the same time capture German submarine bases on the Belgian coast. To ready the British for this great drive took seven weeks. Huge supplies of ammunition were brought to the guns. Artillery was placed hub to hub.

The Germans were prepared. The attack at Messines, when the British had exploded powder under the ridge, alerted them to the direction of the new British effort. German reinforcements marched for Flanders.

When he was ready, General Haig ordered his artillery to fire day and night for ten days. This was to "soften up" the enemy trenches. The German cannons fired, too. It started raining, and the wet clay soil of Passchendaele Ridge in Flanders was churned so thoroughly by the artillery that a man could hardly walk in it.[1] In places, stepping off planks or duckboards meant drowning in the mud.

Max Osborn, German war correspondent, wrote:

... [the British artillery seemed to create] an earthquake in Flanders. ... It is like the bowels of the earth exploding. Our infantry is wait-

[1] See Map No. 15, page 155.

ing. It sits in its dugouts, where it trusts to luck. It is as if it were locked in prison. The men cannot get out, nor can anybody approach them.... Our trenches are spattered with steel splinters, shrapnel bullets, stones, and earth.... No one will ever forget the horror of it.

When the bombardment stopped, the infantry fight started. German infantry reserves marched to the battlefield. They were helped in their counterattack by a novel idea: low-flying airplanes which sprayed British infantry with machine-gun bullets. The Germans also released clouds of mustard gas. This new poison seared the lungs, and when it came into contact with flesh it raised large blisters.

In spite of its great effort, the British gained only five miles in the wet clay soil. This battle in Flanders (sometimes called the Battle of Passchendaele) cost them 300,000 men killed, wounded, and missing. Sixty thousand men were lost on the first day. One British officer wrote of the hopeless attack in the mud, ... *If a careful search had been made from the English Channel to Switzerland, no worse place for an attack could be discovered.* Later, Winston Churchill wrote, *Britain bled herself white at Passchendaele.*

When the frightful casualty lists reached London, Lloyd George moaned over and over, "Blood and mud."

The attack in Flanders failed because the wet clay was poor ground over which to attack. The British paid a high price, but in attacking they saved the floundering French Army. Had the Germans been able to attack the French at this time, the Allies would probably have lost the war.

For a moment the Allied picture brightened. The first American fighting men arrived in France on June 26, 1917. The French went wild with happiness. Paris put away its mourning and celebrated the Fourth of July. On Bastille Day, General Pershing, who had already arrived, reviewed French troops and pinned the *Croix de Guerre* on French warriors. The band played "The Star-Spangled Banner" and the "Marseillaise." French men and women cried with happiness.

More American soldiers arrived in August, but General Pershing insisted that they required further training. The Allies' hopes sank. And bad news arrived from Italy. At Caporetto, in Northern Italy, Austrian and German armies beat the Italians, drove them back, took 275,000 prisoners, and killed or wounded 30,000 others.

General Pershing ordered training camps built in Lorraine, in northeastern France, where his men could train while they waited for more Americans to arrive.

The Allied leaders were desperate. They saw the need to free their armies from the molelike life of the trenches. To overcome the reigning king and queen of the battlefield, the machine gun and the barbed wire, the British decided to use tanks in mass to break the German line. Cambrai, in northern France, was selected as the place for the tank attack, because there No Man's Land had few shell holes.[2]

The tank brought iron plates to the battlefield to protect the attackers. Previously the tanks had been used only singly or in small detachments. Now, over 438 big tanks lumbered forward slowly in the rolling, slightly wooded country. Straight for the German trenches they headed. Bullets rattled against their sides. The tanks lumbered on, grinding up the barbed wire. The British artillery, which had not fired a shot until the tanks advanced, now pounded the German trenches. A smoke screen helped the tanks forward.

But in the center of the line the 51st Highland Division, commanded by an old-fashioned British officer, did not keep up. This general believed that the tanks would prove a hindrance, and he ordered his soldiers to stay back from them at least a hundred yards. When the tanks passed by, the veteran German infantry—surprised but not cowed—had time to run out of their dugouts and fire into the Highlanders. Then more trouble struck on the Allied side. The lead tank, crossing a bridge over a canal, went through the bridge. German machine guns opened up, and

[2] See Map No. 19, page 206.

the Germans sent over gas. The British did not have enough reserves to keep their attack rolling, because of their heavy losses in Flanders, and because they had had to send troops to help the Italians. The battle at Cambrai lasted a week, then the brave British Army was forced back.

The tanks, although they gained only limited success at Cambrai, had been helpful. The Allies increased their manufacture as fast as they could. The Germans, who were short of steel, could build only limited numbers.

The year 1917 closed. Every country in the fighting had lost thousands of men. Germany had gambled in pushing her submarine warfare, and it had brought America into the war against her. The war was developing into a race for time. The Allies desperately needed the American Army to take its place beside their hard-pressed soldiers. The Germans realized that they had to win before a large American force could fight against them.

Both sides flooded their newspapers and newsreels with propaganda. Stories, some of them true, were told of German submarines that had fired on men in lifeboats. Some young French girls living in territory that the Germans had captured were sent into Germany and worked as laborers on farms. The Germans, in turn, told of the inhumanity toward their airmen forced down in enemy country.

The British sense of humor shone through the war clouds and encouraged the Allied world. At the time of the Zeppelin raids the British magazine *Punch* published a cartoon of a young English girl saying at breakfast to her mother, "Oh, Mother, I *do* think it unfair about the Zeppelins! Everybody saw them but me. *Why* didn't you wake me?" Her mother answered, "Never mind, Darling, you shall see them next time—if you're good."

And the cartoons of Captain Bruce Bairnsfather were among the best in history. One in the *Bystander* showed a British "Tommy" writing home. He is sitting on an ammunition box in the yard of a ruined French farmhouse. The dwelling behind him is a shambles. A shell hole is at his feet. A dead cow and horse are close by. He is writing, *At present we are staying at a farm.*

The Allies needed their humor and all the strength they could muster, for the Kaiser had given the strong-willed General Ludendorff his way. Food in Germany was scarce. The Germans realized that their submarine campaign was a failure and that every week more and more American soldiers were landing in France. Ludendorff, a gambler, was ready to risk an all-out attack.

Chapter 22

"RETREAT, HELL!
WE JUST GOT HERE!"

During the Battle of Cambrai an odd thing happened. The
Germans, in counterattacking, made an end run—a wide
one. Some of their soldiers on this sweep through the forests and
fields headed for the village of Gouzeaucourt, eight miles southwest of Cambrai, where the 11th Regiment of United States Railway Engineers worked with the 4th Canadian Railway Battalion
to lay a track over the captured ground. The soldiers saw the
need for their work: they were making it possible for a broad-
gauge railroad track to stretch from Paris to Brussels for the
first time since 1914.

On the ninth day of their work the United States Engineers
were spitting on their hands, with sleeves rolled up, as they
pounded ballast under the ties. They did not know they were
in danger. While they labored, the engineers heard the thunder
and crack of the guns to the north. "That's up at Cambrai," an
engineer officer said. "They're having a time." The engineers
worried about the rumble of the guns, but the work went on.

Gas shells burst in a nearby field, but the wind carried away
the yellow clouds. The engineers grumbled. They wished that
their officers had not followed the advice Canadian officers had
given that morning: "It's best to leave your weapons in camp so
you won't have to worry about them."

Suddenly, shells roared in and iron fragments scattered over
the railroad track. A few engineer soldiers fell. Out of the woods

and across the fields streamed Germans. Some had machine guns strapped to their backs. To fire a gun, the man carrying the gun threw himself down while his partner pressed the trigger. In the front ranks with the machine-gunners were men with flame-throwers.

Some engineers stood their ground and fought with shovels and picks. They had little chance. Some were captured. A curtain of artillery shells sealed off routes to the rear. The roar of the shells and the crack of rifles added to the confusion. A British military policeman, directing traffic at the square in Gouzeaucourt, saw a big truck bearing down on him and waved it on. Too late he discovered it was German, loaded down with enemy riflemen and machine gunners.

Captain Raymond Hulsart, of New Jersey, and First Lieutenant Paul McLoud, of Albany, New York, rushed through the bursting shells to lead the engineers back to camp for their weapons. Hulsart shouldered a wounded man and saved him from capture. In the wild fight, some of the engineers who had been captured, and who were on their way to a German prison camp, escaped and rushed back to the American camp for their rifles. McLoud rounded up men to help hold off the Germans. Standing by him were British, Canadians, and some of his own engineers. The enemy attack finally stopped. A young battalion staff sergeant, John Kieran, who became a famous writer, naturalist, and radio and television star, wrote later of his part in the battle, *I was like General Sheridan before the Battle of Winchester—twenty miles away, armed to the teeth.*

While the fight of the engineers was not a great battle, it was not long before one of the biggest German attacks took place, in 1918.

General Ludendorff had now become the most important man in Germany. His forceful personality made his influence even greater than the Kaiser's. The situation looked dark for the Allies. This was because German troops which had defeated Russia were on railroad trains headed for the Western Front. Ludendorff told the Reichstag, the German parliament, that he was prepared to lose a million men. He planned three attacks. This is the story of those attacks.

General Ludendorff chose an area along the River Somme, roughly sixty miles northeast of Paris, for his first attack.[1] He hoped to knock out the British Army and to drive a wedge between the British and French. Ludendorff's orders stressed surprise. He took his best divisions and retrained them behind the lines. He taught them to seek weak spots in the Allied positions and to pinch off strong points from the rear. The Germans learned how to follow a rolling barrage. That is, how to stay close behind artillery fire moving deeper and deeper into Allied areas. General Ludendorff planned, too, to have a few light, horse-drawn cannons up with the infantry. His idea was to have the guns fire pointblank at machine-gun nests, tanks, and pillboxes.

By questioning prisoners, the British learned of the coming big spring attack. It was a fearful time for the Allies. The United States still had only six divisions in France. The French armies were not in good condition. Their infantry was war-weary and discouraged. The mutinies were over but the morale of the French Army was low. The British were keeping 300,000 soldiers in England. Lloyd George feared that, if he sent them to General Haig, more attacks would be made and more men lost.

On the German side, Ludendorff was using the net of railroads to shift soldiers rapidly to the Somme area. He hoped to beat the British so badly they would never recover.

On the day of his first big offensive, March 21, 1918, a tremendous German cannon, made by Krupp, dropped shells on Paris from a position seventy-five miles from the city. This shocked the world. It seemed incredible that German scientists and artillerymen could arrange such an exhibition. The Allied soldiers called it "The Paris Gun." It rattled Frenchmen's nerves, but did little damage.

[1] See Map No. 15, page 155.

It was the Germans, at this point, who received a bigger blow. Baron Manfred von Richthofen, the Kaiser's favorite ace, was in his red Fokker triplane speeding along at 140 miles an hour. He was in wonderful spirits. The day before he had gone up in the rain and shot down his seventy-ninth and eightieth enemy planes. He had just enjoyed a romp with his dog, "Moritz," and in his pocket was a leave order giving him a vacation and permission to go hunting. The Baron was up with five other pilots, on patrol over the Somme battlefield. Suddenly he was seen going down behind the British lines. What caused his death no one knows. The Germans were amazed and downcast over the Red Knight's death. The British announced that the German Ace of Aces was shot down in combat, but no one knows which British airman or antiaircraft gunner sent him crashing to earth. He was buried by his enemies with military honors, the funeral escort marching with their weapons reversed.

"The Paris Gun" continued to fire. Parisians became used to the explosion of its shells. The Red Knight's name faded from the newspapers. Attention was now riveted on the battle General Ludendorff was starting.

The thunder of the German guns could be heard for miles. Reports drifting back to Allied headquarters told of German successes along the Somme. Ludendorff seemed to be breaking through. Thousands of French families left Paris for safer areas.

The Allies held a hasty conference. Sir Douglas Haig, especially, saw the need for closer teamwork. He pushed hard for a supreme, over-all commander.

The man selected for generalissimo of the Allies in the West was Ferdinand Foch of France. This sixty-five-year-old leader possessed integrity and a desire to win. He was a quiet, dignified soldier, a man hard to rattle, one who could be stubborn. He was a general who might make mistakes, but he would never become discouraged. Generals Haig, Pétain, and Pershing became his "lieutenants." Making Foch generalissimo was a step toward unity.

Ludendorff and his Germans read press releases telling of the

Allied Supreme Commander, but it did not worry them. They worked to create a gap between the British and French armies—at great cost. The Allies rushed men to the danger points by rail, and successfully plugged the breach. Sixteen days from its start the German attack finally stopped. The British were reeling, but their army was not destroyed.

The Germans failed to break through all the way largely because of British courage. The Kaiser's Army was still the best in the world, but its iron discipline and its supply system were growing weaker. When it overran British supply dumps, it forgot its orders to continue to attack. Its men were hungry, and they sat down to eat.

The Germans had traveled fifty hard miles from the twenty-first of March to the fourth of April, 1918. Newspapers in the United States featured this achievement. The Germans captured 70,000 prisoners and inflicted 200,000 casualties. Although Germany paid a high price for the gain (over 200,000 casualties) the Kaiser was happy. He sent for von Hindenburg and pinned on his broad chest the Iron Cross with Golden Rays. Erich Ludendorff, the brains of the offensive, stood by while von Hindenburg received the glory. Soon the Kaiser had Ludendorff planning the next battle.

Ludendorff was like a boxer who, in the middle of a fight, decides to try a new attack to knock out his opponent. He switched his might to Flanders and attacked along the Lys River. As a change of pace, he used ideas General von Hutier used in Russia: secrecy, surprise, men going forward in many small units with the artillery fighting hard to help the infantry forward.

The Allied cause hung by a thread. World War I had become a great American Crusade, but thousands had time to go to baseball parks to see Babe Ruth, the home-run hitter. Many United States newspapers devoted more space to the marriage of Charlie Chaplin, an actor, than to the six United States divisions in France.

Portuguese soldiers in the Allied lines, and the French and

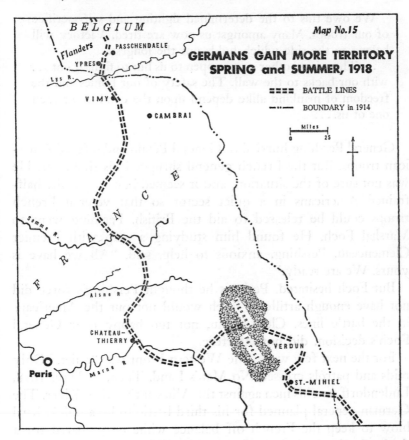

British, fought for every inch of the line, but Ludendorff's power roller ate up more ground. The war seemed lost for the Allies. The British had every man available in France in the line. The determination of the British leader, Sir Douglas Haig, showed when he stiffened his men with an order:

TO ALL RANKS OF THE BRITISH ARMY IN FRANCE AND FLANDERS
Three weeks ago the enemy began his terrific attacks against us on a fifty-mile front.... In spite of throwing already 106 divisions into battle and enduring the most reckless sacrifice of human life, he has as yet made little progress toward his goals.

We owe this to the determined fighting and self-sacrifice of our troops. Many amongst us now are tired. Victory will belong to the side which holds out the longest.

... There is no other course open to us but to fight it out ... with our backs to the wall. The safety of our homes and the freedom of mankind alike depend upon the conduct of each one of us. ...

General Pershing hurried to General Pétain and offered American troops. But the French general shrugged his shoulders. He was not sure of the situation, and it seemed best to put the half-trained Americans in a quiet sector so that veteran French troops could be released to aid the British. Pershing went to Marshal Foch. He found him studying a map with Premier Clemenceau. Pershing, anxious to help, said, "All we have is yours. We are ready."

But Foch hesitated. Perhaps he thought Pershing's force did not have enough artillery. Foch would not put the Americans in the battle lines. Clemenceau, not too happy over General Foch's decision, did not interfere.

For the next few weeks the Western Front was "quiet." Only raids and patrols crossed No Man's Land. Then, in May, 1918, Ludendorff sent his men against the Allies at the Aisne River. The German general planned for his third battle to be a quick, hard blow to keep the French off balance while he prepared for a final offensive against the battered English.

Thirty German divisions hurled themselves at the French. The Germans captured 60,000 prisoners, 650 heavy guns, machine guns numbering 2,000, aviation material, ammunition, and supplies of all kinds. The Kaiser's men gained forty-five miles. The German Crown Prince was in command at the front, under Ludendorff. The soldiers of the Crown Prince pushed on, arriving at Château Thierry, less than forty miles from Paris. The French were frightened. More of them left their homes.

General Pétain called on General Pershing for help. The American commander rushed the Second and Third Infantry

Divisions toward Château Thierry. Trucks were used to transport the soldiers, and part of the move was made at night. There was confusion. The roads were crowded with refugees and French troops retreating. Men, women, and children were filled with terror because of the Germans just behind them.

Suddenly, the refugees and the French soldiers saw the Americans. Many peasants did not know American troops were in France. Long columns of Americans, hurrying forward from their trucks, were singing. The "Yanks" looked strange to the French because not all of them had received steel helmets. Some wore steel helmets borrowed from the French, others wore wide-brimmed brown campaign hats, a reminder of the Western Plains.

The Second United States Division, with its Marines, arrived near the village of Château Thierry in time to see the last French troops leave for Paris in a panic. The Germans were at the Marne River, at the north side of town.

A French officer ran to the Marine 7th Machine Gun Battalion. "You had better retreat," he said.

A Marine officer drew his pistol and drawled, "Retreat, hell! We just got here!"

Marine Captain Lloyd W. Williams countermanded an order to retreat which a French officer gave to his unit.

The appearance at Château Thierry of the two United States divisions was dramatic. French soldiers took heart. The Germans were stopped. They had outrun their supply lines, and they were surprised by the fierce attack of the Americans.

Floyd Gibbons, a war correspondent with the Marines near Château Thierry, was impressed with the wonderful *esprit de corps*—the spirit of the unit—of the Marines. Gibbons, in the Marine front line, had his left eye shot out. It was feared he was dead. His "last" dispatch was cabled to the United States, where it received wide publicity. In praising the Marines at the expense of the infantry, Gibbons sowed seeds of jealousy. No one fought more bravely than the United States Marines near Château Thierry, but they formed only two of the eight regiments of the Second and Third United States divisions which stopped the Germans at the Marne.

Five miles west of Château Thierry lay a square mile of hilly, rugged forest. This was Belleau Wood. American patrols discovered it was a German strongpoint jammed with machine gun nests. The tired French gave the job of recapturing Belleau Wood to the United States Marines. Brigadier General James Harbord, who had escaped from his supply duties, commanded them.

On their way to the Wood, the Marines met more refugees and some French soldiers who were fleeing. The frightened French shouted in panic-stricken manner, *"La guerre est fini! La guerre est fini!"* (The war is finished!) *"Pas fini!"* (Not finished) the Americans answered. Later the Americans nicknamed the area "The *Pas Fini* Sector."

When the Marines entered Belleau Wood, they were greeted by roaring machine guns and gas. The rattle of the weapons resounded in the ravines. Gunnery Sergeant Fred W. Stockham, of Detroit, Michigan, saw a wounded Marine whose gas mask had been shot away. The disabled Marine was breathing poison gas. Sergeant Stockham did not wait. He pulled off his own gas mask and gave it to the wounded man. Then Stockham directed the removal of wounded men to a safe place and helped carry them out of artillery fire which was shattering trees in the area. He reeled from the effects of the gas, but he worked on. A few days later Sergeant Stockham died a horrible death from the effects of the poison gas. Later, President Wilson ordered that his memory be respected by the award of the Medal of Honor.

In the fighting, a Marine battalion advanced directly into the enemy's machine-gun fire. The combat was hand-to-hand. The farther the Marines advanced into the Wood, the heavier the German machine-gun fire became. The Germans had their automatic weapons placed so that they supported each other. The Marines captured Belleau Wood. However, 55 per cent of the Marines were casualties. The American Lieutenant General

Hunter Liggett wrote later that the deaths at Belleau Wood were an unnecessary sacrifice.

The bravery of the American soldiers at Château Thierry and Belleau Wood made the world regard the war in a new light. The Allies applauded the Doughboys and Marines. General Pétain published an order praising the fighting of a machine-gun battalion of the Third Infantry Division. "The Tiger," France's great patriot, Premier Georges Clemenceau, journeyed to the headquarters of the Second Infantry Division. He said, "I have come to see the brave Americans who saved Paris."

The third German drive had been stopped. Two things had occurred: the Germans had outrun their supplies, and the counterattacks by the Americans at Château Thierry and at Belleau Wood halted them forty short miles from Paris.

Chapter 23

THERE IS NO SUBSTITUTE
FOR BRAVERY

EVEN before the fighting at Château Thierry and Belleau Wood, Americans met the test of the battlefield.

The First Division had marched to shell-torn land sixty miles northwest of Château Thierry. When the 28,000 men of the division were in the trenches alongside French Colonial troops, the French general commanding sent the First Division a message: *The soldiers of France welcome you. We salute your flags which unfold themselves on the soil of France.*

The Germans sent a different kind of welcome: ninety batteries rained mustard-gas shells. The Germans had discovered that artillery shells were a better means of spreading gas than letting it escape from cylinders and float across No Man's Land.

The bloody work went on twenty-four hours a day. At night patrols from both sides fought for control of No Man's Land. In the daytime, German planes peppered the Americans with bullets. American aviators, formerly of the famous French air unit, the Lafayette Escadrille, now fighting under the American flag, flew their planes to protect the division from low-flying Fokkers.

This was a defensive sector, but the artillery fire on both sides was tremendous. The German held the high ground around the town of Cantigny, and this was an advantage to them, because they could see everything the Americans did.[1]

[1] See Map No. 16, page 172.

The scream of German shells through the air, and their crack when they burst above the trenches, made sleep impossible for the Americans, except in deep dugouts. The cooks at the kitchen wagons, far to the rear, were able to send only one meal a day to the men in the front-line trenches. Water for washing was unknown. Truck drivers and teamsters in the ammunition train drove their vehicles at night, without lights, over shell-pocked roads, to bring ammunition to the front. One of the problems was to take back the wounded. Also, the brass artillery shell cases had to be carried to the rear so they could be sent to factories and reloaded. Life in the trenches was a hardship, an ordeal. It seemed, as it always does in battle, that the best officers were being killed. The men of the First Division began to look forward to attacking the enemy on the high ground.

Finally a secret message arrived. The division was ordered to capture the high ground near Cantigny. This was important, but far more important was the question, *"Were United States soldiers good enough; did they have the training and courage to capture a German fortified hill?"*

Colonel Hanson E. Ely, of Iowa, a real leader of men, and his 28th Infantry Regiment were selected to lead the fight. To make sure the attack was successful, his regiment was first withdrawn from the lines. They were marched to ground far to the rear which resembled Cantigny, where they rehearsed their attack against trenches built like the German system.

The Allied generals pointed out that the American artillery would play an important role. The infantryman in the front lines had a real friend in the artillery leader of the First Division. This was a vigorous officer from Florida, the son of a private in the Confederate Army, Charles P. Summerall. In the Philippines years before, young Summerall disapproved of the artillery's "war of their own." He wanted the gunners to help the infantry forward. The soldiers of the First Division nicknamed him "Sitting Bull," but he was anything but a sitter. His bravery was established. In the Boxer Rebellion, seventeen years before, young Summerall had commanded a section of "Reilly's Battery." In the attack on the walled city of Pekin, Summerall walked through the fire of the Chinese sharpshooters to the huge gates. He chalked large "X's" on the hinges for his gunners to aim at, so their guns could batter the gates down. Captain H. J. Reilly demanded that his cannoneers be experts. He wanted them models of perfection. General Summerall, at Cantigny, France, held his First Division artillery to the same standard.

Zero Hour for the attack at Cantigny was 6:45 A.M., May 28, 1918. In the American lines only men without nerves slept. Summerall's artillery pounded German artillery; it placed gas and smoke shells on areas where German reserves were waiting.

The First Division was a team. When the watches of the infantry platoon leaders ticked to 6:45, the infantry rose in three lines and followed French tanks and Summerall's rolling barrage.

The fight at Cantigny was at close quarters. German prisoners were captured. Flame-throwers seared Germans who refused to come out of the dugouts. When the Americans captured the fortified hill they dug trenches as fast as they could to protect the town from a counterattack. The next wave of Americans strung protective barbed wire.

A German rolling barrage crept toward Cantigny. Behind it marched waves of German infantry.

For three days and nights the First Division fought for the ground they had won. The fight cost the First Division forty-five officers and 1,022 men killed, wounded, or missing. The battle was called a "local affair," but it proved that the American soldier could attack and win.

After the battle, on his way to the rear with his men to rest, General Summerall stopped to visit a field hospital. One of his artillerymen lay on a bloody stretcher. The general knew the soldier was dying. The soldier opened his eyes and said, " I know you. You are General Summerall. If you stay with me I won't be afraid to die." The general knelt beside the stretcher. He prayed quietly. Charles P. Summerall served the United States in its army for forty-three years, from West Point plebe to

Chief of Staff in Washington. This was his most heart-rending moment.

American airmen had a harder time making their mark than the Doughboys. This was because when war was declared the United States did not have a single plane worthy of aerial combat. The country that had invented the plane was far behind the rest.

General Pershing was not sure how much American airmen could accomplish. He wrote his friend, General Mason M. Patrick, [*The aviators*] *are a lot of good men, but they are running around in circles. Someone has to make them go straight.* Pershing gave the job to General Patrick, an Engineer officer. Eventually, the Air Service, A.E.F., helped beyond Pershing's dreams.

American aviation had a champion—the dynamic, often irritating, colorful Colonel William Mitchell. In France, Mitchell was the third-ranking American aviator. He was impatient for United States pilots to take their place in the front rank of the war. Even though Pershing signed a contract with the French for 5,000 planes, at a cost of $60,000,000, Colonel Mitchell believed American aviation could accomplish more if given freer rein and more planes. However, Pershing was not too interested. Aviation was just one of a thousand things in his mind.

To ready himself for the day when he would be a leader in aerial combat, Mitchell went to the front-line trenches. He was fearless and imaginative. To show the beloved Brigadier General Stuart Heintzelman, important staff officer, the value of an aerial view, Mitchell flew him over No Man's Land.

For Billy Mitchell, an aviator's life was the only life. He said, "The only romance in this war is in the air." He looked down on the infantry. Although he nettled many ground officers, Mitchell saw the worth of the plane as a weapon. He could see over the horizon.

Finally, Colonel Billy Mitchell was given a chance to control combat pilots. He was placed under an old soldier, General

Hunter Liggett of Pennsylvania. Liggett listened to Mitchell and tried to help him develop an air force that could strike. Some considered General Liggett too fat to fight, but not Mitchell. They liked each other and worked together in harmony.

Each week Mitchell's pilots did better. One of the most successful had been an automobile test driver from Indianapolis and Columbus. His name was Eddie Rickenbacker. He had a slow start in the war, for he was General Pershing's chauffeur. Eddie hated waiting, and there was much of that. Finally he obtained a transfer to the Air Corps. He rose rapidly in rank and, because he was smart and a winner, he became a captain. At night, he worked to check every round of the ammunition he would fire the next day, to insure that every round was perfect. His Hat-in-the-Ring Aero squadron, with its insignia of Uncle Sam's hat in a ring painted on the fusilages, became famous. Rickenbacker, a lean, hungry-looking fighter, was unafraid to take chances. He earned the Medal of Honor for attacking seven German planes singlehanded over No Man's Land, sending two of the planes to earth in flames.

As the war progressed, American aviation became better. There were hard fighters in the Air Corps, men like Captain Fiorello H. LaGuardia (later Mayor of New York City) who led bombing raids against the Austrians, and Major Raoul Lufbery, who had fought in the French Foreign Legion. Men like these started Army Air Force traditions of bravery in combat.

Some of the pilots led a gay life while off duty. This was before they realized that to fly a plane and fight they had to be in top mental and physical condition. Some lacked discipline. Second Lieutenant Frank Luke, a blond cowboy from Arizona, was one. He irritated most of his fellow officers with his cocky, overconfident air. But no one questioned his fearlessness.

One day Frank Luke took his single-engine biplane up. He had no orders. Luke was spoiling for a fight, and he thought he knew where there were German observation balloons. He had downed German balloons before. The press called him "The Balloon Buster." Luke liked that. Most pilots disliked fighting balloons because well-aimed fire came from them, and because they were protected.

Luke flew over soldiers in the trenches, men of the Rainbow Division. When he saw a line of six balloons, he flew through antiaircraft artillery fire, and that can be frightening. Fire from the balloons streaked at him.

He closed in and cut loose with his machine gun. Three balloons burst into flames and sank to earth. German Fokkers, on guard high in the sky, left their cloud cover and dove at him. The battle noise resounded for miles. Luke shot down two Fokkers before one closed in, guns blazing. A German bullet hit Luke and wounded him.

Frank kicked the rudder of his Spad and flew toward his home airdrome. His wound hurt. Blood oozed to the floor of the cockpit. The wound felt as if it were on fire. It was hard to fly. He fought to sit upright. *If I can only keep this ship up,* he thought.

Down on a dirt road leading to the German trenches, Frank Luke saw a company of infantry on the march. It was clear. They were reinforcements. He sprayed them with machine-gun bullets—then had to land.

The captain of the German company said to one of his lieutenants, "Go. Take a squad and bring in that American aviator."

Frank Luke crawled from his wrecked plane. Blood was spurting from his wound. He drew his caliber .45 pistol.

The German lieutenant approached Frank under a white flag. With the German were seven soldiers, rifles at the ready. But Frank was in no mood to parley. He fired a clip of seven rounds at the Germans, and they killed him.

Later, his memory was honored by a Medal of Honor. Men still talk of his deeds. Lieutenant Frank Luke was not disciplined, but there was no more devil-may-care, fearless pilot in any air force.

Chapter 24

AMERICANS AT THE MARNE

MAJOR HARRY J. KEELEY, a young West Point graduate from Illinois, listened to the staff officer. The staff officer, a lieutenant colonel from Third Division headquarters, talked about a captured German major. "A brave guy. We picked him up yesterday. He swam the Marne River so he could scout this ground." The staff officer waved his hand carelessly toward the flat country to the front. He nodded at the edge of the forest where Keeley's battalion of infantry was eating supper.

Keeley's heart quickened. "I hope you learned something from him," he said.

"Plenty," the colonel said. "His maps and papers show that their main push is coming right through here. And this fellow talked. He believes they're going to win. He says Ludendorff promised the German Army that this attack will be a 'peace offensive.' They think they'll push right through us and march on Paris."

Little Harry Keeley's blue eyes snapped. He had a flip-floppy jaw and he waggled it in his funny way. "When they comin'?" he asked.

The staff officer stood up. "Soon. We believe everything this captured Heinie said because German deserters say the same thing. Our aviators report they've got troops moving up. It all fits in. They'll probably lead off with a heavy bombardment."

Keeley lit a cigarette. The lieutenant colonel's words were bad news, but there was nothing Keeley could do about it—except fight.

The staff officer leaned against a poplar tree and looked down the line of zigzag trenches Keeley's infantrymen had dug along the edge of the wood. Keeley's battalion of the 38th Infantry, almost one thousand strong, was eating steaming-hot "slum"—a beef stew that had been carried up from rolling kitchens three miles back. The steel helmets of the Doughboys looked like shallow dishpans.

The staff officer squatted and gazed over the plain to the front, toward the Marne River. "You have a good field of fire." He checked his watch. "I have to be going, Shorty." The lieutenant colonel gripped Keeley's hand. "Good luck," he said. "I like your position. Hang on."

Shorty Keeley watched the staff officer mount his horse and trot away with his orderly. For a second young Keeley allowed himself to think of the comforts the staff officers had at division headquarters, then Keeley looked at his grimy infantrymen sitting along the top of their trenches and in the woods just to the rear. Keeley loved his soldiers. He felt like the father of a large family. His men believed in him and looked to him for leadership.

The soldiers finished their supper and washed their mess kits in a stream. An evening breeze chased the heat of the July sun. A quartet sang:

> Pack up your troubles in your old kit bag
> And smile, smile, smile. . . .

A private brought Shorty Keeley a mess-kit of stew. The soldier sat on a log beside Major Keeley, hoping the major would say a word. The soldiers liked Keeley, liked the salty way he talked, liked the funny way he moved his jaw from side to side.

"Everything's all right, ain't it, Major?" the private asked.

Keeley put his tin spoon into the stew and tasted it mechanically. *A heavy bombardment,* he thought. *"I like your position,"* the staff officer had said. *But is it all right? The edge of the*

woods? From across the Marne River it must look like a target.
"Sure we're all right," he said to the private. "Get me all the officers. We're movin' the heck out of here."

So, at dusk, Major Keeley, trusting his own judgment, gave orders to his captains to move the one thousand men and their weapons forward five hundred yards, away from the trees.

"Hate leaving these trenches, sir," a captain protested. "Could be a mistake."

"Don't think so," Keeley said. He waggled his jaw. "Safer away from the edge of this forest. These woods are a target. When we get on the new line, have the men dig in—fast."

Young Keeley's battalion, in moving forward from the prominent forest, was adding strength to the idea of General Gouraud. Gouraud, a one-armed, determined Frenchman, was in command of the sector. He arranged the Allied soldiers "in depth"—that is, the front-line trenches were an outpost, and the main battle positions were 2,000 to 3,000 yards in the rear. He had his artillery distributed in depth, too, so it could fire on the enemy at almost any point. Gouraud was a stout-hearted fighter. To him, a retreat was an eternal blot on a man's character and honor.

Keeley, and thousands like him, waited nervously for the attack. Each hour seemed an eternity. At ten minutes past midnight, the German artillery thundered. Thousands of shells from heavy cannons plunged down on the edge of the woods which Keeley's men had abandoned. A gas sentry of Keeley's, in a shallow foxhole, beat an iron pipe, *dong-dong-dong*. A wooden claxon rattled. The infantrymen struggled into their gas masks and readied their rifles. The masks felt clammy.

At three-thirty in the morning the concentration of German shells swept back from the edge of the woods to the shore of the Marne River, then moved inland again and bombarded the forest. Automatic rifles from the German side of the river sent streams of bullets whipcracking over Keeley's battalion.

Smoke covered the river, and through it, every now and then, you could see small assault boats crowded with German soldiers paddling for the Allied side of the river. Temporary foot bridges were hustled up by the Germans behind the smoke and placed in the water. German infantry rushed across.

Keeley's men crouched in their shallow, newly made foxholes and took a toll of German infantry.

Keeley's battalion and other battalions of the 38th Infantry Regiment were bombarded, but held. The Germans rushed by them—but they did not pass through them. The Americans held.

General Gouraud's artillery fired curtains of flaming iron at the German artillery.

Among the Allies fighting at the Marne to stop the so-called "Peace Offensive" were Frenchmen and Italians. The Italians ran; part of the French were overrun.

The men of the Forty-Second (Rainbow) Division, representing every state in the Union, clung to their battle positions, roughly forty miles east of the Third Division. The Rainbow soldiers fought with ball ammunition, and when the Germans closed in they fought them with trench knives, pistols, bayonets, fists, teeth, and rifle butts. In the battle, as division chief of staff, was Colonel Douglas MacArthur, a brave officer who liked to go out on patrol with the soldiers. In World War II, he became a great leader and a General of the Army.

On the Marne battlefield, with the soldiers of the Rainbow Division, was a priest, Father Francis Patrick Duffy. He was a warm man with a glib tongue, a man who loved humans so much he had to steel himself to bury the dead. The soldiers liked to have the lanky Irishman near them. They loved to hear him sing. He earned the Distinguished Service Cross for extraordinary heroism, and General MacArthur recommended that Duffy be placed in command of the "Fighting Sixty-ninth" regiment of infantry. But Father Duffy himself stopped that. "My calling," he said, "is this." He touched the symbol on the front of his overseas cap, a small silver cross.

At the Marne River, Father Duffy was up and down the trenches of the Rainbow Division cheering the men, like a fine quarterback encouraging his football team during a goal-line stand.

Finally, the German attack floundered and stopped. Both sides had suffered.

American casualty lists at the Marne brought the war home to people all over the United States. In the Third Division, the 38th Infantry Regiment alone, 3,800 strong, lost 1,199 in killed, wounded, and missing. Among its heroes who were decorated later with the Silver Star medal for gallantry in action was Major Harry J. Keeley.

Major General Joseph T. Dickman, of the Third Division, reported to General Pershing:

The 38th Infantry wrote a brilliant page in American military history. It prevented the crossing of the river at certain points while, on either flank, the Germans who gained a footing pressed forward. Our men, firing in three directions [as the Germans streamed by] . . . threw two German divisions into complete confusion, capturing six hundred prisoners.

The entire Third Division fought bravely. It earned the title of "Marne Division." Other soldiers, of other American divisions—the Twenty-eighth and Forty-second—did their share.

General Gouraud, his empty left sleeve tucked in the pocket of his blue-gray coat, came to see the tired soldiers of the Forty-second Division. He said, "In this Second Battle of the Marne, the men of the Rainbow put a new spirit into France. I thank you."

On the German side, the great German general, Ludendorff, was not disheartened by the Battle of the Marne of 1918. He said he considered it only a minor affair. It was soon clear that he had ordered the attack because he hoped it would draw Allied reserves, and he hoped they would come from the British front. It was against the British in northern France that Ludendorff planned to launch his final, win-or-die attack.

The Germans were stopped at the Marne, but they had driven a pocket into the Allied lines on the south bank. General Foch studied his map. He wondered what he could do to straighten out the new dent in his lines.

Chapter 25

SPEARHEADS AT SOISSONS
AND ST. MIHIEL

FLASHES of news were given to front-line Americans: Nicholas Romanoff, the Czar of Russia, and members of his family, were executed by the Soviets. . . . Mr. Herbert Hoover, who is helping transport food from the United States to Europe, said that most of the 80,000,000 bushels of wheat sent to the Allies in the past year represented the sacrifice of American men, women, and children, who helped by not eating white bread. . . . Lieutenant Quentin Roosevelt, son of ex-President Roosevelt, was killed in aerial combat. The German press reported, *"On July 14, not far from the Marne, an American Squadron of twelve battle planes was trying to break through German air defense. A noncommissioned officer in a German flying machine shot down young Roosevelt's plane over German lines. The remains of the brave young airman were buried with military honors."* . . . A German newspaper, the *Deutsche Zeitung*, reported that a feeling of depression over the unfavorable course of the war was flooding the German nation.

Marshal Foch decided that he could add to the depression of the Germans by flattening out the bulge in the Allied lines between the Aisne and the Marne Rivers. With care, he drew arrows on his map to show his army commanders how they would attack.

The main blow would be near Soissons, France. Spearheading

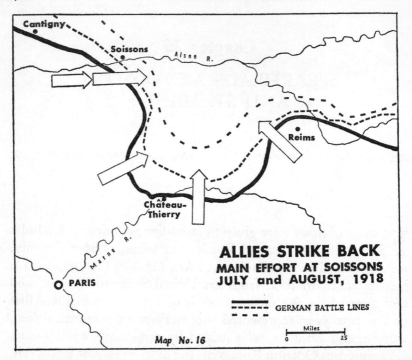

ALLIES STRIKE BACK
MAIN EFFORT AT SOISSONS
JULY and AUGUST, 1918

------ GERMAN BATTLE LINES
- - - -

Miles
0   25

Map No. 16

the attack were the 1st and 2nd United States Infantry Divisions, and French soldiers from Morocco. Four-fifths of the spearhead was American. The great thrust was commanded by General Mangin, of the French Army.

General Charles Summerall was now leading the force he loved, the First Division. He had his horse-drawn 75- and 155-millimeter cannons placed skillfully. With the aid of mathematics, he located the guns so that their fire could be switched to any part of the enemy trenches.[1] Summerall arranged for one infantry regiment to go forward while another assisted it with all its fire power.

The attack started at four thirty-five in the morning, on July 18, 1918. It was dark, but the artillery fire seemed to set the clouds aflame. French tanks, their machine guns rattling, crawled

[1] This was the start of an innovation in skillful use of field artillery, the beginning of the artillery fire direction center.

toward the enemy lines. Red rockets arching into the sky signaled for more Allied batteries to fire. The dawn and the bombardment painted the heavens blood red.

German machine-gunners opened up on French tanks, and in turn were knocked out. In the advance, one company in the First Division lost fifty-seven men without firing a shot. The 2nd battalion of the 16th Infantry Regiment was almost annihilated. The dead and dying dotted the farmland; the screams of the wounded made a fearful accompaniment to the shells. Enemy aircraft roared overhead. They bombed and machine-gunned the Americans advancing through a wheat field. Wounded crowded the first aid stations. The attack went on.

The 18th United States Infantry fought bravely. At the end of the second day, a messenger in the uniform of the famous French Foreign Legion appeared at the post of command of the colonel of the 18th Infantry. The private saluted the colonel and handed him a message. *The Foreign Legion considers it not only a privilege but an honor to fight by the side of the gallant troops of the 18th United States Infantry.*

The price of the five-day fight, in the First Division alone, was 234 officers and 7,083 men killed, wounded, or missing.

The Germans pulled back slowly and skillfully. On August 6, 1918, Foch's map showed that the bulge in the Allied line at that point was flattened. But more important to the Allies, the Germans abandoned their plans to attack and crush the British in Flanders. The plans for attack by the Germans were collapsing; they would now have to stop the plans of the Allies.

General Pershing went to Marshal Haig, of Britain, and to Foch, of France. He told them that United States soldiers had proven themselves on the battlefield, that they had won the right to fight as a separate army. Pershing pointed on the map at St. Mihiel, a French town twenty miles south of Verdun. The bulge in the German lines there was a dagger pointing at the heart of France. The American leader suggested that his men flatten out the German lines in the area about St. Mihiel, and then push ahead. The Briton and the Frenchman agreed.

The Germans had held the ground at St. Mihiel for four years, and had organized it well. Their trenches were sturdily built. Their gunners knew the range to every point of the ground. General Pershing and his staff worried. They had enough infantry, but infantry needs help to advance. Pershing's army lacked tanks, artillery, and planes.

General Pétain rushed to Pershing and loaned him this equipment, and men to operate it. General Pershing and his men got ready to strike.

Then Marshal Foch came to General Pershing's office. "The Germans are disorganized," Foch said. "The British attack at Amiens, in the north two weeks ago, captured 15,000 Germans and 400 guns in one day. German deserters say that Ludendorff called the victory the 'Black Day.' When his men retreated, they called to other Germans marching to the front, 'You're prolonging the war.' " Foch banged his palm against the table. "General," he said, "let us push hard. Give the German Army no rest."

Pershing agreed, but he disagreed violently when Foch explained that he wanted to split the American Army into three groups. It was the old argument again. Ferdinand Foch said that the American Army did not have enough artillery. General Pershing's temper rose. He said that the United States had sent troops to France in the order the French had requested them.

The two leaders became angry. Foch's mustache seemed to bristle. Finally he said, "I must insist on my arrangement."

Black Jack Pershing's turtle-like jaw snapped. "Marshal Foch, you may insist all you please, but I decline to agree to your plan. Our army will fight wherever you may decide. But it will not fight except as an independent American Army."

The argument went on. Foch said he had ideas of a better and more advantageous attack, in the Argonne Forest. But finally it was decided that the attack would be at St. Mihiel and that it would be limited to merely flattening out the German line.[2]

General Pershing ordered skilled field artillerymen aloft in the

[2] See Map No. 15, page 155.

planes. His idea was that they would be observers and would radio back to the batteries information about American artillery fire so that it could be accurate. Lieutenant Lawrence ("Biff") Jones, of Washington, D.C., was one of the observers. Before young Jones went aloft he thought of the enemy antiaircraft fire, so took along an iron stove lid to sit on. After the war, he became a famous football coach at West Point, Louisiana State University, Oklahoma University, and the University of Nebraska.

Pershing gathered all the artillery he could find. He even arranged for French artillery to help. He ordered the American infantry to go "over the top" at St. Mihiel at five in the morning. It was September, 1918. Charles Hawkins, a young wagoner (a truck driver, who held a rank equal to corporal) from Brooklyn, New York, said that the artillery fire was so intense you could read a newspaper by the flash of the guns.

In addition to heavy artillery fire and planes in the skies helping his infantry forward, Pershing had 267 tanks. The infantry loved the slow-moving monsters because they punished enemy machine guns.

The planes were commanded by Billy Mitchell. He had assembled a most unusual air division: Americans, British, French, Italians, and Portuguese. He worked hard and succeeded in welding the different nationalities into a unit.

The attack was a success. However, it must be said that it was helped by the Germans themselves, because they were leaving the area. Pershing's men captured 15,000 prisoners.

The Allied generals were impressed. They saw now, without doubt, that the Americans could fight as an army. Foch was not petty-minded. He hastened to Pershing and congratulated him.

Foch told of his next plan. He wanted Pershing to attack north from the Argonne Forest.[3] This meant moving a quarter of a million Frenchmen out of the area between Verdun and the Argonne and moving over a million United States soldiers there

---

[3] See Map No. 17, page 178.

from St. Mihiel. The moves would have to be made rapidly, before the Germans could bring up reserves.

This meant shifting the American Army at night by rail, trucks, and marching. The Heights of the Meuse River in the Argonne was outlandishly rugged country. Few Americans knew what awaited them.

Chapter 26

THE LOST BATTALION

THE Argonne Forest covers a stretch of mixed-up hills. The forest land looks as though it has been rumpled by an earthquake. This tangled territory in eastern France was the battleground for one of the hardest fights in the history of the United States Army.

When Foch gave Pershing the order to attack to the north in the Meuse-Argonne country, Pershing and his staff saw the danger: they had to make a straight-ahead attack. It had to be a piledriver smash into three carefully laid-out German defense lines. There was no other way. Numbers of people still wonder why Pershing accepted such an assignment.

The task of moving over a million soldiers from St. Mihiel to the Argonne was gigantic, and took three weeks. The men were moved at night so the Germans would not discover the shift. The difficult planning was done by a young colonel, a graduate of Virginia Military Institute, George C. Marshall. In World War II he became Chief of Staff of the Army, wore five-star-rank insignia, and was later Secretary of State.

Intelligence reports said, and they were true, that the Kaiser's men had labored four years to build the Meuse-Argonne fortifications. They had converted woods and hills, and such stone houses as there were, into strong points. They had piles of every type of ammunition on hand. They were ready for any attack.

Among the Americans approaching the jumping-off line in the Argonne were men who called themselves "New York's

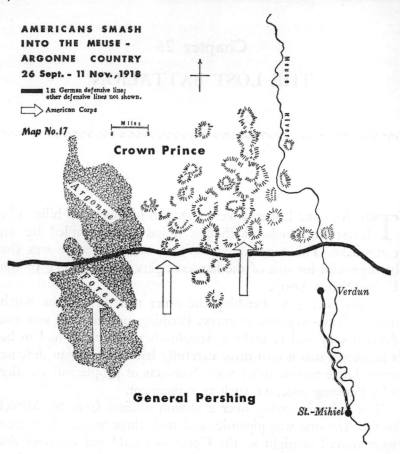

AMERICANS SMASH INTO THE MEUSE - ARGONNE COUNTRY 26 Sept. - 11 Nov., 1918

■■■ 1st German defensive line; other defensive lines not shown.

⟹ American Corps

Map No. 17

Miles 0 5

Crown Prince

Argonne Forest

General Pershing

Meuse River

Verdun

St.-Mihiel

Own" (the Seventy-Seventh Division). They were proud of their yellow and blue shoulder patch—the Statue of Liberty. The soldiers of the 1st Battalion of the 308th Infantry Regiment liked their leader, a lanky, studious-looking fellow from Pittsfield, Massachusetts. "Galloping Charley," they called him, because of his long legs and quick walk. He did not talk much, but every man in the battalion believed in Major Charles W. Whittlesey. The major reminded them of a kindly schoolteacher. When he adjusted his glasses and looked at you, you felt as though he were reading your secrets.

The attack into the forest started on September 26, 1918, with shooting that sounded like the end of the world. The Americans and the French smashed the first two German lines of defense. But Pershing's tanks broke down, conquered by the rough ground. Supplies were hard to bring up over the country roads. The Americans soon became thankful for skimpy meals of corned beef—"Corned Willie," they called the canned meat— and hardtack. Ammunition supply became perilous. It was hard to bring the wounded out.

On the morning of the third day, New York's Own ate breakfast in the rain. But their spirits were not dampened. The men joked, "Part of our breakfast is the cannon barrage." *It is pretty cold*, Major Whittlesey wrote in his diary.

Captain George McMurtry, of Pittsburgh, Pennsylvania, a broad hulk of a man with high cheekbones that gave him the appearance of an Indian, walked among the men. The soldiers liked George McMurtry. He never talked down to them, and when he told them what was up he spoke confidentially, as if he were a father telling his family a secret. McMurtry, who looked like a husky halfback in prime condition, was an officer men would follow anywhere. "Galloping Charley" depended on Captain McMurtry, who was next to him in rank.

After breakfast, Whittlesey's men and men from other units, 700 all told, pushed ahead through the wet woods. Captain Nelson M. Holderman, of Santa Ana, California, expert woodsman, led one of the columns. He made the men be quiet and warned them that stepping on twigs might alarm the Germans.

But where were the Germans? Whittlesey and his men could hear firing on both sides. Whittlesey stopped. He cleaned his eyeglasses and talked the mystery over with Captain McMurtry. The husky, Indian-like McMurtry agreed that the thing to do was to push on ahead.

Major Whittlesey's battalion reached the knifelike ridge it was to take, but neighboring units on either side did not.

There were Germans in front of Whittlesey's battalion. Just before dark both sides fired. In the morning, the men found more Germans in front of them, and also on both sides. A few more were in back of the battalion. "Galloping Charley" sent a combat patrol under one of his best lieutenants, Arthur McKeogh, to clear out the Germans in the rear. With Lieutenant McKeogh went linesmen to string telephone wire back to regimental headquarters.

The woods echoed shots fired by both sides. "Galloping Charley's" long legs carried him along the sides of the ridge so he could check his battalion.

The telephone men came back. "We don't have enough wire to reach," they told the major.

Lieutenant McKeogh and his patrol returned. McKeogh was wounded. One of his patrol was dead. "The Germans are closing in," the lieutenant gasped. "Hundreds of 'em."

More Germans came. They surrounded the "Lost Battalion."

"Dig in," Major Whittlesey ordered. Each man dug a rifle pit and later labored to connect them with trenches. The hand entrenching tools of some of the men clicked on granite blocks of an ancient Roman road. Whittlesey's men were in a rough oval. They were in all-around defense, something like the wagon trains of the pioneers at night on the Western Plains when there was danger of attack by Indians. Like the plainsmen, Whittlesey's men were "within the circle."

German bullets whined and zip-cracked. They plowed into the dirt on the tops of the rifle pits. Branches fluttered down on the men. The Statue of Liberty men captured a German and brought him to Major Whittlesey. "Mister Major," the prisoner said, "you will be wiped out."

"Keep quiet," the major snapped.

"Yes, indeed," the prisoner answered.

Cries of "Surrender, *Amerikaner*," came from the woods.

"Galloping Charley" wrote a message to each of his captains and sent it to them by runner: *Our mission is to hold this position at all costs. Have this understood by every man.*

Machine guns raked the Lost Battalion. The ravine rang with the roar of guns. The Americans fired rapidly to keep the

Germans from coming closer to the ridge. To get water cost a life or a wound. You had to crawl down a ditch to the slimy water at the bottom of the ridge to fill your canteen. Private Judd's body was sprawled there—a silent warning. First aid bandages were used up. When more men became wounded the bandages were taken from the dead.

Whittlesey ran along the position to the fire pit, where Private Omer Richards, a French-Canadian, had a cage of homing pigeons.

"Get a bird ready," the major said. He wrote a message on tissue paper, describing the battalion's position in the woods, and asked for help.

Private Richards folded the message and reached into the cage. "Not you, Cher Ami," he said, pushing Dear Friend gently to one side. "Your turn will come later." The private reached for another pigeon. He folded the message, tucked it in a tiny capsule, and fastened it to the bird's leg with a tin clip. When Richards released the pigeon, it circled the Lost Battalion, then flew over the Germans toward the regimental headquarters far to the rear. "He has a built-in compass," Richards explained to Major Whittlesey.

The men of the battalion suffered at night for lack of blankets and from mortar shells. The moaning of the wounded was a fearful sound. At daybreak, Whittlesey poured some ground coffee into his canteen cup with a little precious water, and muddled the mixture with a stick. He drank the coffee slowly. Whittlesey prayed that help would break through the ring of Germans. He wrote out a message for another of Richards' pigeons to carry: ... *Send food, blankets and overcoats. Whittlesey.*

The major prayed that his message would get through. He questioned Private Richards.

"Zese are ze best birds in France," Richards assured him. "My pigeons love flying to zat loft. It's like home to zem. And when zey enter a little trap door, a bell rings. Ze pigeon-handler undoes ze message and phones it to headquarters. My birds are my best friends."

"*Our* best friends," the major said.

German fire on the Lost Battalion became heavier. Another pigeon flew through the woods carrying a plea for help.

Billy Mitchell's pilots flew over the treetops, through German rifle fire, to drop food to the battalion, but the food fell on the Germans.

The nights were wretched. Fires to keep the men warm were impossible. "They would only bring death," the major told them.

Another pigeon flew to its loft with the message: *Need rifle ammunition and hand grenades. Have nine men dead and 140 wounded.*

Wrap leggings were now used for bandages. American rescuers tried to fight their way through to the Lost Battalion, but the Germans blocked them. A cold rain drenched both the foe and Whittlesey's solders. The dwindling ammunition supply worried the major and his leaders.

An American soldier who had been captured by the Kaiser's men walked out of the woods toward the Lost Battalion. He waved a tiny white flag. He handed Major Whittlesey a message which read:

SIR:

...The suffering of your wounded men can be heard in the German lines. We are appealing to your humane sentiments to stop. A white flag shown by one of your men will tell us that you agree to these conditions. Please treat this soldier as an honorable man. We envy you.

Whittlesey tightened his belt. He was exhausted from lack of sleep and tortured by strain. "We will not reply," he told Captain McMurtry.

When their message was not answered, the Germans charged. The Lost Battalion greeted them with rapid fire. In the German attack were flame-throwers belching liquid fire. Captain

McMurtry ran along the embattled line to check the men and to encourage them, although he was wounded in the knee and was suffering. A fragment from a German hand grenade hit him in the shoulder. He fell on his face. Blood poured down the side of his coat. He got up and moved a machine-gunner to a better place so he could fire more accurately.

Captain Nelson Holderman, of Company "K," forgot his three wounds when he saw two wounded Statue of Liberty men suffering in one of the rifle pits under heavy artillery fire. He struggled to the top of his trench, rushed through artillery and machine gun fire to the men, and carried one of the wounded to a safer place. Then he went back for the other one. When the German attack was beaten back, Captain Holderman helped to move more wounded, although his own wounds felt as if they were on fire.

Whittlesey's company commanders ordered the ammunition checked and distributed so that each man would have some. The men were exhausted. They worried. "Supposing the Germans attack again?" they asked the major as he checked the rifle pits.

Whittlesey was almost gay. "Keep your spirits up," he said in his firm but quiet way. "Two million Americans are working to rescue us." He sent another message by pigeon asking for help.

Cruel "help" came. An American barrage pounded the Lost Battalion instead of the Germans. Whittlesey wrote frantically on tissue paper: *Our own artillery is shelling us. For Heaven's sake stop it.*

While the major was writing his message, Private Richards worried, for pigeons need exercise if they are to fly, and Richards' pigeons had been cooped up in their wicker basket for four days. Richards and his helper, Private Tollefson, had never seen a pigeon penned up longer than seventy-two hours and still fly when released. Richards pointed at the bigger of the two pigeons he had left. "We'll save Cher Ami for ze last," he said to the major. "She's a beeg girl. Zat bird'll fly if she has to stay in cage a week."

When Richards opened the basket, one of the pigeons fluttered out before Richards or Tollefson could grab it. The bird scurried along the ground, then managed to flap to the top of a tree. Richards cursed.

Only Cher Ami was left. Private Richards cuddled the bird as he clipped on the message capsule. "Cher Ami, dear friend," he whispered, "you must fly. You must get through."

Artillery cracked and thundered overhead. Iron fragments tore through the trees. A man nearby screamed. A tree crashed to the ground. Machine-gun bullets spattered mud over Richards. He released Cher Ami. The pigeon rose slowly, flapping its wings hard. The Germans fired at it, but Cher Ami escaped and flew toward its loft. A shell screamed into the shallow trench and took off Private Tollefson's head. Richards gathered up the pigeon food and ate it.

Major Whittlesey ordered the dead all along the position covered with branches and leaves. He visited his wounded. Their condition racked him. He had no doctor. The first-aid men did their best. The major was like a father, sometimes tender, sometimes stern. "No surrender," he kept saying. "We will not surrender."

German snipers crawled into better positions. On some parts of the ridge it was certain death if you moved in daylight. The Kaiser's men inched closer. They bombed the Lost Battalion with hand grenades. "Surrender!" they called.

The suffering of the Americans on the shell-torn ridge became greater. They were hungry, tired, wet, and frightened. They wanted water. It seemed to them as if they had been under fire a lifetime. First Sergeant Jim ("Cream Puff") Carroll left the battalion at night to search the enemy dead for food. The wiry first sergeant was anything but a "cream puff."

On the fifth day, American rescuers broke through. Of Whittlesey's 700 men who went through torture, only 194 walked out, and some of them were wounded. Among the men walking to safety was Captain McMurtry. He limped along, refusing a ride on a stretcher. "There might be another fight," he said.

Back in the States, headlines screamed of the rescue of the

Lost Battalion. When he heard the details, President Wilson ordered that the Medal of Honor be given to Captains McMurtry and Holderman and to Major Whittlesey.

Among the many Americans fighting in the Argonne was Captain Harry S. Truman, a battery commander in the 35th Division. Later he became President of the United States. Another was a Dartmouth College man, Frank W. Cavanaugh. He volunteered for France, although he was the father of six children. "Cav, the Iron Major," became one of football's greatest coaches at Boston College and later at Fordham. His career as a football leader was shortened because of blindness caused by the wounds he received in World War I.

Part of the enemy in the Meuse-Argonne was the ground over which the drive took place. It is unbelievably rugged.

The fight in the Argonne is an American epic, and one of its proudest stories is how a turkey-shooting Tennessee marksman shot his way into history.

Chapter 27

SERGEANT YORK OF TENNESSEE

ALVIN C. YORK sported a red mustache and a private-first-class chevron. He was a husky, over six feet. The men in his company liked him because there was nothing put-on about Alvin York. He was modest, and had a plain, honest look.

Army life bothered York. Soon after he arrived at Camp Gordon, Georgia, and joined the 82nd Division, he went to see his company commander. Alvin saluted and said, "Sir, Private York has the first sergeant's permission to speak to the company commander."

"What is it?" the captain asked.

Alvin talked quietly. "I have to have out, sir. I can't stand getting ready to fight. It's against my religion to kill a man. I want to leave the Army."

Captain E. C. B. Danforth, of Georgia, was patient. He argued with Alvin but made no headway. "It's your duty to fight for your country," Danforth said.

"It's agin' the Old Book," Alvin replied. "I have to leave."

Major George E. Buxton, the battalion commander, listened to Alvin, too. Both officers knew that York was the best rifle shot in the eight-hundred-man battalion; they realized times were not far off when the battalion would need men who could shoot like him. Major Buxton took York aside. They talked for long hours.

After several days of arguing, Buxton said, "Tell you what I'll do, York. I'll give you a two-week furlough. Go home and think things over. Talk to your preacher, and pray to the Lord for guidance. We know you are honest. When your leave is up, if you still think you can't fight to defend your country, tell me and I'll try to get you out. I do not know if I can do it or not, but I'll try."

When Alvin York returned, after two weeks at his home on the wild Wolf River in Tennessee, he announced that he was ready to fight. Captain Danforth promoted him to second-in-command of a squad of eight men, and York sewed private-first-class chevrons to the sleeves of his uniform, below the red, white, and blue patch of the 82nd Division.

The soldiers of the 82nd called themselves "The All-American Division," but most of them were from Georgia, Alabama, and Tennessee. By October, 1918, the division had proved itself twice under fire, at Lorraine and at St. Mihiel. It was a hard-fighting unit.

Now, marching on winding French roads, the soldiers could hear the rumbling of the battle ahead. Their officers passed the word down from Major General George B. Duncan, the division commander, "We are going into the Meuse-Argonne. Rough fighting ahead."

The Argonne Forest is hilly, rocky woodland. Hill follows hill in endless procession. The land looks as if an angry giant had rumpled it up. It is a crazy-quilt country, carved by ravines. The men of the AEF found the Germans in the best places, their machine guns sighted to mow down attackers.

The 82nd took up extended order formations and advanced. They found the fight hot. The Germans were counterattacking, trying to win back lost ground. The 82nd Division stopped the counterattack and inched ahead. The crash of the battle resounded against the hills and in the valleys. Artillery cut down trees. Bullets whipcracked and whined off the rocks. Men went down. The wounded screamed. Some were carried by brave stretcher bearers through the fight, back to first-aid stations. Others died where they fell.

In the battle in the tangled-up country there was confusion.

Alvin York could not find his corporal. He worried. German machine guns up ahead chattered, and every time they rattled Americans died.

Private First Class York took command of his squad. He told his seven men, "Come on with these other guys. We have to get those guns. Follow me."

York's squad was part of a patrol of seventeen. They worked their way forward. Without knowing it, they pierced the enemy line. Just ahead was a clearing, and in it stood a large number of Germans listening to one of their officers. Obviously, the German major was telling them what to do.

The American patrol walked into the clearing, rifles pointed at their enemies. The Germans threw up their hands. Suddenly, a machine gun up on a hill fired and nine of the Americans fell, killed or wounded. Both Germans and Americans threw themselves on the ground to escape the deadly fire. Alvin crawled behind a dead body and opened fire at the machine-gun nest. Fifteen Germans appeared in the sights of his rifle and fifteen died.

After putting the machine gun out of action, Alvin ordered the Germans lying nearby to stand up. He and his patrol started back to the American lines with the German major and his men. Some of the Germans were helping wounded Americans.

Alvin York was on the side of the column of prisoners. Just when it appeared that he and his friends would arrive safely with the prisoners, six Germans jumped out of a trench and sprinted down a path, straight for Alvin. The German in the lead emptied his pistol at Alvin. The bullets hit near his feet, but Alvin York kept cool. He aimed and shot each of the six Germans through the head.

"I used an old turkey-shooting trick," he said later. "Shot the hind ones first so the front ones wouldn't take heed. Didn't want them to know they was in danger."

"Did you use a gun sling?" York was asked.

" 'Twarn't necessary," he drawled. "Warn't time."

A few minutes later, more Germans held their hands up to Alvin. "*Kamerad!*" they shouted. "We surrender!"

The Americans marched the prisoners back to Captain Danforth. Private Alvin York and his men had four German officers and 128 men.

Nearby was Lieutenant Joseph Woods, inspector from division headquarters. He checked the details of York's feat of courage, sharpshooting, and leadership. Others verified them. On General Pershing's recommendation, Alvin York was awarded a Medal of Honor.

Captain Danforth promoted him to sergeant. Major Buxton praised him and shook his hand. Both officers felt rewarded. Their patience and understanding had enabled the modest Tennesseean to become one of the greatest heroes of the war.

Chapter 28

AMERICAN FIGHTING MEN

THE punishment the Americans were taking in the Argonne was reflected in the casualty lists. The rumpled-up country aided the defenders. Their automatic weapons were sighted over the barbed wire, and they had arranged their soldiers so that, if the attackers managed to crash through anywhere, more defenders waited to kill them.

The American artillery smashed into the German fortifications, and the American infantry attacked straight ahead. There was no other way to win. The battle sounds echoed and re-echoed in the hilly country.

As the battle went on, the Americans were divided into armies. General Pershing selected two of his best leaders as commanders, Hunter Liggett, of Pennsylvania, and Robert Lee Bullard, of Alabama. But in the fighting there was little a general could do. He could arrange for tired units to receive rest; he could make certain that ammunition and food reached his fighters; he could put in reserves to influence the battle; and that was about all. The actual winning of the fight rested with the leaders who were closest to the troops, as it usually does. These leaders are the noncommissioned officers, the lieutenants, and the captains.

Billy Mitchell, the air leader, flew over the battle. He scribbled a note while in his plane: *The Infantry is knocking its head against a stone wall.*

Mitchell helped by borrowing 322 bombers and their pilots from the French. He organized an air armada of bombers protected by fighter planes, and helped the American infantry by bombing German reserves. Then his armada flew on to wreck German flying fields.

Like pilots in every World War I air force, Colonel Mitchell's pilots paid the penalty for flying rickety machines. With the wind shrieking through the wires bracing the wings, and the force of the air against their faces, the pilots experienced frightening sensations of speed. When a pilot crashed, Mitchell ordered his body recovered, if it were possible, and buried in a cemetery at Toul, in northeastern France, not far from the German lines.

One of his pilots was the colorful Major G. Raoul Lufbery of Wallingford, Connecticut. As a young man Lufbery had knocked about the world. He learned to fly in India. He gave flying exhibitions in China and Japan. When war broke, Lufbery enlisted in the French Foreign Legion and rose to the rank of sergeant. He transferred to the Lafayette Escadrille and became an "Ace." His playmate was the Escadrille's mascot, the tiger cub "Whiskey."

Lufbery conceived the idea of having planes that were hard pressed by enemy air fly in a circle, each plane protecting the one in front. "The Lufbery Circle" tactic was adopted by the United States and other air forces.

When General Pershing approved the transfer of numbers of Americans in the Escadrille to the American air service, Lufbery was on the list. He became a major and shot down plane after plane. But one day in 1918 he met his death when he was defeated in close combat by a German Albatros two-seater. A French girl arrived at the wreck long before anyone else and covered his body with flowers. His death was a loss, for not only was he America's leading pilot at the time, but he had the knack of helping others. Lufbery could relate his experiences in the air in such a way that they became lessons for others.

Colonel Mitchell personally arranged for the funeral. Eddie Rickenbacker flew the lead plane of a formation over the grave and bombarded it with flowers.

In the First World War, there was unusual challenge and

romance in the air services. The most successful pilots were daredevils, sometimes unruly. They often fought in unorganized combat in the air, with no relation to the fighting on the ground. Colonel Mitchell was a showman, driven by ambition, but he saw the problems of the future as well as the present. He wrote, *Just think what it will be in the future when we attack with one, two, three thousand airplanes at a time.* ... When he organized his air armada to help in the battle in the Argonne, Mitchell was ahead of his time.

A lieutenant colonel with the tanks in the Argonne, just as much a showman as Colonel Mitchell, was George S. Patton, Jr. When many of his tanks floundered on the Argonne hills, he left them and rounded up infantrymen who had become disorganized. He led them behind the few tanks still grinding on. A bullet wounded him. Patton, a young Californian, served notice that he could help the United States. He was of even greater value in World War II when he became a general.

A most unusual fighter in the Argonne was a red-faced young lieutenant with a powerful body, Sam Woodfill. Woodfill left his home in Indiana and became a Regular Army sergeant. He fought Moros in the Philippines and served in Alaska. When the United States entered the world war, Woodfill became a "Ninety-day wonder," earning his gold second lieutenant's bar in a training camp.

Sam Woodfill, now a first lieutenant, was leading a company of the 5th Division when his platoon was stopped by machine-gun fire. To escape, Woodfill fell into a shell hole. The bullets zipped two feet overhead. Then they tore up the dirt around the little crater. The bullets seemed to be searching for him. Sam took out his wife's picture and scratched out a note:

In case of death, it is my last and fondest desire that the finder of my remains shall please do me the everlasting favor of forwarding this picture to my darling wife. Tell her I have fallen on the Field of Honor. ...

The machine gun that was torturing him switched its fire elsewhere, and Sam escaped death. Next morning when a machine gun killed men of Sam's company, he decided he had had enough of German machine guns. So he took two privates with him, and they worked their way around through the trees until they were on the side of the machine-gun nest. Sam shot three Germans who were at the gun. When his company advanced, Sam rushed ahead through the fire and wrecked another enemy machine gun and its crew. A few minutes later, he charged a third machine-gun position. In the hand-to-hand fighting he used a rifle and a pick, in turn, as clubs, until he was finally able to draw his pistol and shoot the last German who faced him. Miraculously, Sam escaped death.

When General Pershing heard that Sam Woodfill had killed approximately fourteen of the enemy and had captured three more, he personally checked on the young soldier and his deed. The general called him "the outstanding soldier of the A.E.F." Lieutenant Woodfill was awarded the Medal of Honor.

After the war, a French general who had read Woodfill's Medal of Honor citation discussed his exploit with General Pershing. The Frenchman had translated "singlehanded," to mean "one-armed." "You mean to tell me, General Pershing," the general said, "that Woodfill killed all those men with only one arm? Marvelous!"

General Pershing, whose French was as poor as the French general's English, answered, "He certainly did."

Fighters like Sergeant York, Lieutenant Woodfill, Lieutenant Luke, Captain Eddie Rickenbacker, Captain Holderman, Captain McMurtry, and Major Whittlesey were given the highest American decoration. Six Americans serving with the Canadian Army won the Victoria Cross, the highest military medal of the British Government. The world saluted the courage and bravery of American fighting men.

The British had seen this bravery before the First World War. They had seen it in the French and Indian War and in the Revolutionary War. This bravery stood out in the winning of the West, in Cuba, in the Philippines, and in China. In France, thousands of Americans proved what well-trained, disciplined Americans can do under fire.

In every war, many acts of bravery go unrecognized because they are never written down. There is usually no time to describe courageous actions so that higher commanders can review them and award medals.

Often bravery is unrecognized because it is commonplace. For instance, Private Joe Pascale, of Philadelphia, told of his service in the Meuse-Argonne with the 28th ("Keystone") Division. "The Argonne was an awful place. Hills and hills, covered with trees, ravines, and machine guns. One day, they asked for volunteers from my company to go back and bring up the mail. I wasn't looking for a particular letter, but I volunteered. On the way back, snipers got to firing at us, and that's lonely. A machine gun barked at us. Then we ran through artillery fire. When we arrived at the rear headquarters there wasn't any mail. Instead, they loaded us up with ammunition and food like pack horses. The return trip seemed rougher. I got to thinking, 'Where will I be if a bullet sets off this ammunition?' That weighed me down more than my load. When I finally got back, the first sergeant yelled, 'Hurry up! Pass out that ammunition to the first platoon. You can leave that chow here.' "

Among the unsung groups of men who displayed bravery and courage every day their unit was in the line were the forward observers for the artillery. These soldiers were trained to work their way up front to positions where they could see the results of the artillery fire. They telephoned corrections back to the batteries on wires laid on the ground. Corporal Ted Speers, a young man from Princeton University, said of his experience as a forward observer in the Argonne, "My job was to help lay telephone wire. At one place, for a short time, some of our artillery was out in front of our infantry. This was because our battery commander wanted to fire on a railroad seven miles behind the German lines. The guns needed to be close up front because of the range. Pulling wire over the ground with the Germans on a hill just across the Meuse River made us feel scary. At night, one of their shells hit one of our tractors towing a gun and set the tractor afire. It blazed like a beacon. Our infantry complained bitterly." After the war Ted Speers became a famous Presbyterian preacher and, later, chaplain to the West Point cadets.

Bravery and teamwork of thousands of Americans paid off in the fiery furnace of the Argonne. In desperate and exhausting fighting, through unbelievable country, the Americans cleared the forest of Germans. This was a blow to the Kaiser and his generals.

But the progress of the First United States Army in the Meuse-Argonne was slow, which irritated the old "Tiger of France," Georges Clemenceau. He gasped when he saw the report, *America is suffering over 100,000 casualties in the Argonne.*

The "Tiger" rushed to Marshal Foch and said excitedly, "Pershing must go! Take steps to get him relieved."

But Foch knew the kind of country the Americans were up against, and the strength of the German field fortifications, and he refused to act. Marshal Pétain also turned a deaf ear to Clemenceau. The "Tiger" hurried to see one of the leading generals of the Allied War Council, an American from Pennsylvania, Tasker H. Bliss. The "Tiger" unburdened himself, angrily. But Bliss supported Pershing. So did Secretary of War Baker, and Pershing stayed.

Chapter 29

ATTACK IN THE DESERT

I N the meantime, the British battled the Turks in the rugged Holy Land. This was a strange campaign. It is a story of a great general, of a weird but effective raider, of Arab tribes, of soldiers of many nations, and of sacrifice and suffering.

The British were determined not to lose the Suez Canal. Troops and food from India, New Zealand, and Australia were shipped through it. There was also the matter of pride. Protecting the Suez called for hard fighting, some of it in temperatures over 110 degrees, fighting in which a drop of water in a canteen was as precious as a bullet in a rifle. The battles took place over 800 miles west of Kut, the desert town where the conceited General Townshend surrendered his soldiers to unspeakable tortures by a cruel Turk.

The campaign started when 20,000 Turks marched through the deserts of the Sinai Peninsula toward the canal in early 1915, dragging their boats over the sand. A German, General Kress von Kressenstein, assisted them by furnishing leadership and knowledge.

When the Turks reached the Suez they hoped to stage a surprise night raid. They launched their boats quietly. They were happy when nature favored them with a dust storm.

But lookouts on British and French warships gave the alarm. Searchlights etched the boats of the Turks. Gun crews, afloat

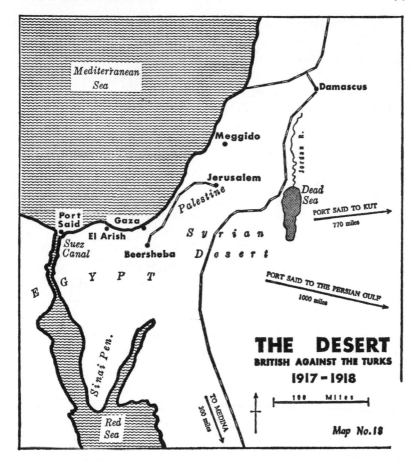

Mediterranean
Sea

Damascus

Meggido

Jerusalem

Palestine

*Dead
Sea*

PORT SAID TO KUT
770 miles

Port
Said   **Gaza**

El Arish   *S y r i a n*

*Suez
Canal*   **Beersheba**   *D e s e r t*

PORT SAID TO THE PERSIAN GULF
1000 miles

E   G   Y   P   T

Sinai Pen.

THE   DESERT
BRITISH AGAINST THE TURKS
1917 - 1918

TO MEDINA
300 mile

100   Miles

*Red
Sea*

Map No. 18

and ashore, slammed home powder bags and shells. British soldiers from India, manning shore batteries, played the major part,
and the Turkish boats sank.

The surprise attack of the Turks in 1915 made the British
think. The few Turks captured were poorly equipped, their
uniforms in rags. They were hardy but were not well fed.
If the Turks could cross the trackless sands once, who knew
but that they might not return?

The British decided not to sit and wait on the west bank of
the canal. They thought it best to defend it by advancing to El

Arish, where they could control the routes to the Sinai Peninsula.

So that the British could move into the desert, water pipe was
transported from the United States. The British laid the pipe
and built a railroad alongside it. Turkish raiders slashed at the
work, but were driven off. The prize for the fighting was El
Arish, and the British won it by December, 1916.

Lloyd George, the Prime Minister in London, was delighted.
The Allied cause needed a victory after the slaughter on the
Somme and the fall of Rumania. He felt he could find it in the
desert. Therefore, Mr. George ordered the British to proceed into
Palestine. But he failed to give them the necessary reinforce-
ments.

The first attack on the Turks, in their positions from Gaza
to Beersheba, failed. And trouble came out of the British reports
describing the battle. British General Sir Archibald Murray
exaggerated his descriptions, and the War Office thought he had
won. Murray neglected to tell how the heat and shortage of
water had weakened his soldiers and animals. In every war, un-
truthful reports have caused trouble. Murray was aghast when
the War Office asked him to push on almost a hundred miles
and capture Jerusalem.

Murray's army was in no condition to go forward, and,
worse, the Turks and von Kress strengthened Gaza and Beersheba. The Turks and their German leader were taking no
chances that Murray might capture the precious wells.

Murray plunged on. The battle for Gaza cost the British
Empire almost 6,500 soldiers, and the city was not captured. General Murray was recalled to London and a real leader replaced
him, General Allenby.

Sir Edmund Allenby, nicknamed "The Bull" because he was
huge and forceful, was the perfect leader for a desert campaign.
He was careful yet imaginative, kindly yet irritable, hard but
understanding. The first thing he did was to visit each of his
units. Like Pétain after General Lanrézac had been replaced,
Allenby worked to restore the spirits of his soldiers. He saw

their needs and labored to supply them. He demanded reinforcements, and received them. His leadership breathed new life into
his army. And he was under pressure. Lloyd George said he
wanted "Jerusalem by Christmas." There was work and fighting
to do.

While Allenby was making plans for the campaign, he was
visited by one of the strangest characters ever to fight for any
army, Thomas E. Lawrence, who bore the nicknames "Lawrence
of Arabia" and "Wrecker of Engines."

Young Lawrence wore the headdress and flowing robes of
the Arabs. He was only five feet tall, but he was tough, wiry,
and fearless.

The Bull listened to the captain seated before him. Lawrence's
story was as odd as his costume. Barefooted in his Arab dress,
with a curved dagger at his waist, Lawrence of Arabia looked
like a native prince.

General Allenby wrinkled his brow. In thirty years in the
King's Army he had never seen anything like this. Before
Allenby and Lawrence met, staff officers had informed the general that Lawrence was a show-off; that he was undisciplined;
that he did just as he pleased; that his nervous giggle made him
impossible. They said that Lawrence should be taken down a peg
or two, and at least taught how to salute. They said that he had
a cruel streak, that he had ordered that wounded Arabs be shot
rather than have them taken prisoners by the Turks. "Where
does he get authority for such acts?" they asked. "Why not
put this show-off back in uniform and discipline him?"

Allenby thrust out his jaw. He knew that the little captain
was a genius at guerrilla warfare. There were a number of other
British officers on duty with the wild Arabs, but none got
along better with them than "El-Aurens." Lawrence, working
with the Arab chieftains like Feisal who were strong enough to
control their tribes and make them forget their hatred of each
other, was wrecking Turkish railroad trains.

The Arabs were untamed. A joke in camp was to set a friend's
tent on fire. Once on the march some of Feisal's men saw some

camels belonging to another tribe. They rode their camels after the strays. When Feisal called for his men to stop and they did not obey, he threw his rifle to his shoulder and killed the man farthest out. The rest whirled back into the column.

Although the Arabs were fighting the Turks for freedom, many Arabs owned slaves. They even gave two to Lawrence for his use while on campaign.

General Allenby knew that Lawrence could speak Arabic after a fashion, and that he had gone into the homes of the Arabs and made friends. With the help of chiefs like Feisal, the tall leader of many moods, Lawrence led the Arab Revolt against Turkey. Sometimes Lawrence and his chieftains commanded 8,000 men, sometimes 2,000. On raids against the Damascus Railroad they blew up over seventy bridges. The Turks ached to capture Lawrence. They offered $100,000 if he were captured alive, or $50,000 for his head. These rewards were a temptation for the poverty-stricken tribesmen, but not one yielded to the lure.

Allenby helped Lawrence. The general was not bothered by the raider's "uniform" or by his unmilitary customs. General Allenby gave him rifles, camels, field guns, ammunition, food, dynamite, and money. The amount of credit the general arranged for Lawrence to draw on was huge: $1,500,000.

Because of the raids by the Arabs, life for the Turks at Medina, at the end of the railroad, became uncertain. "We want to be careful we don't make them give up the railroad to Medina," Lawrence said. "We want to be just tough enough so they will have a hard time keeping a force at the end of the line. Let's make them spread out their men."

The Turks sent hundreds of groups into the deserts to protect the supply trains, yet the Arabs and Lawrence wrecked them. The Turks set traps for "El-Aurens," but he did not quit. The only thing Lawrence feared was a humdrum existence.

The captain told The Bull how he attacked in the cool of the night. The camels were hidden in a dry wash, perhaps a mile from the Turkish camp, where the groans of the cantanker-

ous beasts could not spread an alarm. Perhaps the hillside shelter-
ing the camels was dotted with waxlike night-blooming cereus.
Lawrence and his scouts crept like wolves to a place where
they could spy on the bivouac of the Turks. The routes of the
sentinels were studied. When Lawrence returned, he told his
Arabs how to attack and win. He usually led the front wave.
The next day, when Lawrence and his raiders were aboard their
camels searching for more Turks, they could look back and see
buzzards circling over the battlefield.

Captain Lawrence, traveling the limitless desert, was not
unlike the jerboa, a desert rat with oversized hind legs that
moves in amazing leaps. The land in which Lawrence operated
had once been grassland, but now its sands shifted and formed
dunes. The wasteland, caused by centuries of overgrazing, had
been a cradle of civilization and culture. Now it was the scene
of cruel warfare in which capture meant torture. Once, when
Lawrence found a wounded Arab, who had been captured by
the Turks, staked to the desert with bayonets through his shoulders and legs, he caused a Turkish column traveling through the
desert to be machine-gunned. Almost two thousand Turks were
slaughtered in this ambush.

Captain Lawrence made General Allenby see the importance
of the Arab Revolt. "Give me airplanes and I'll do more," he
said. The desert raider was happy to receive two fighter planes
and a bomber, because they gave his Arabs "eyes" and a long-
distance striking power.

Lawrence's task was hard. The possibility of treachery always
hovered over him. He took risks in order to make the tribes
attack. For two years his life was rigorous and dangerous. Some
British officers despised him. They were jealous and hated his
methods, but Allenby appreciated Lawrence's work, his bravery,
and the information he brought.

The British general worked to ready his army for a campaign
to the north. He was a dynamo of energy. Units were trained
in desert warfare. Allenby extended the railroad to insure that
there would be supplies. He built the water pipeline far into

the barren country so that water from the Nile would be available to his soldiers and to the horses that dragged his artillery, his cavalry mounts, and his animals working to carry supplies from the railroad.

Turkish spies reported the pipeline. This was bad news for the Turks, for there was a legend that when the waters of the Nile arrived in Palestine the Turks would be defeated. But more important than a legend, Allenby's army outnumbered the Turks almost two to one.

Lawrence played his part in the campaign. With two thousand Arabs mounted on camels, he sliced the Turkish supply line. The Turks suffered for want of equipment and food.

The Bull struck at dawn on the last day in October, 1917, surprising the enemy. Allenby sent some of his cavalry, dragging brush behind them, off to make dust clouds so the Turks would think he was moving in a different direction.

Australian cavalry made a brave charge and captured Beersheba. This gave General Allenby's men the most precious commodity in the desert: water.

Allenby gave his men no rest. He pushed on and attacked the Turks from the west and the south at Jerusalem. When the city fell, before Christmas, Allenby's name was the biggest in the Holy Land. Jerusalem awaited the entry of this modern Crusader. General Allenby was expected to dash in with a cavalry escort, but he walked.

Allenby and the British Army, with the help of the Arabs, gave the Allies the Holy City, but it was a political prize, one which was of scant aid to the over-all Allied effort. It hurt the Allies actually, because it took men and supplies from the British Army in France.

A year later, with Lawrence and his Arabs cutting the railroad in the rear of the Turks, Allenby fought the battle of Megiddo, north of the Dead Sea. The force fighting under the British leader was a mixture: British infantry and yeomanry ("National Guard" cavalry); Seaforth Highlanders from Scotland; Australian and New Zealand cavalry; Indian Lancers (cavalry); foot soldiers from India; South African artillery and infantry; West Indians; French; a few Armenians and Italians; and the Royal Fusiliers. This last regiment, with old traditions behind it, had soldiers recruited from Jewish populations of the big English cities. Pilots and planes of the R.A.F. stood by, ready to do their share.

The supply force was as odd a mixture as the fighters. Boatmen from the Tonga Islands in the South Pacific were used to land supplies along the coast, through the surf. Egyptian laborers and the Camel Transport Corps handled other supplies. You can imagine General Allenby's leadership; he welded the motley force into an army.

In the famous Battle of Megiddo, a soldier from India, Ressaidar Badlu Singh, rivaled Sergeant York and Lieutenant Sam Woodfill. A squadron of the 14th Lancers, fighting dismounted, was stopped by Turks on a Jordan Valley hill. Every time a Lancer exposed himself, well-aimed machine-gun fire rattled, and the Lancer fell.

Ressaidar became angry. He decided to do something. He collected six other Lancers. They crawled as far as they could, then rose to their feet and charged. The machine guns chattered. The Indians captured the hill, but their brave leader was killed while attacking one of the guns single-handed. The King of England ordered that the memory of this Lancer be honored by the award of the Victoria Cross.

At Megiddo, Allenby broke Turkish power in Palestine. General Liman von Sanders, who helped the Turks, was almost captured.

When the Turks were trying to escape after the battle, British pilots caught masses of them in narrow passes in the hills. The pilots slaughtered the Turks with machine gun bullets and bombs.

Allenby's peculiar army captured 76,000 prisoners. The British paid by having almost 6,000 killed, wounded, or missing. Allenby moved on and took Damascus.

Later, the English king sent for Lawrence of Arabia in order to give him the high Commandership of the Bath and the white and gold cross of the Distinguished Service Order. But Lawrence, always a puzzle, refused the honors a few hours before the scheduled ceremony. The British people were shocked. So was Winston Churchill. Lawrence was Churchill's guest at the time. In a private talk with the King, Lawrence tried to explain his actions. No one is certain what Lawrence said, but he probably told the King that this was his way of protesting because the Arabs had, in his opinion, been treated unfairly. They had not received the freedom they expected.

Lawrence of Arabia was an odd individual, expert at guerrilla warfare, but an eccentric so peculiar that no one was certain what he might do next.

The strong man of the victory in the desert was General Sir Edmund Allenby. His victory at the Battle of Megiddo, along with defeats in northern Greece and in the Mesopotamia desert, knocked Turkey out of the war.

Chapter 30

ARMISTICE

WHILE the United States Army attacked with all its might in the Meuse-Argonne, Marshal Foch and Field Marshal Haig hoped to win in the north. The two arrows on the map represent the main attacks. In the northern pincer were about 51,000 American soldiers helping the British. The two pincers were not expected to come together, but it was clear that each attack would assist the other.

Foch studied war constantly, and because he was able to serve amiably alongside the colorless but staunch fighter, Haig, they were a splendid team. The French believed in Foch, and Haig had nerve. With Pershing busy in the Meuse-Argonne, Haig and Foch decided to attack the Hindenburg Line at its strongest point.

If Sir Douglas was worried, and he probably was, he did not show it.

Haig had lost the confidence of the British political leaders and had been warned that there could be no more long lists of dead and wounded. He knew that failure of the great attack would be the end of his career, yet he persuaded Foch that the attack should be made. The British field marshal was afraid of nothing, Lloyd George included.

The St. Quentin Canal, in the Hindenburg Line, was an odd passage. Part of it ran underground. The Kaiser's soldiers living in the canal tunnel were safe from the heaviest bombardment. In it they had storehouses for ammunition and food, offices,

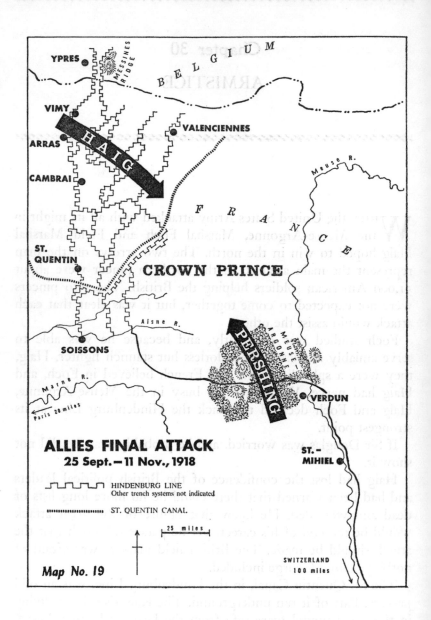

BELGIUM

YPRES

MESSINES RIDGE

VIMY

HAIG

VALENCIENNES

ARRAS

CAMBRAI

FRANCE

Meuse R.

ST. QUENTIN

CROWN PRINCE

Aisne R.

SOISSONS

MEUSE – ARGONNE

PERSHING

Marne R.

Paris 20 miles

VERDUN

ALLIES FINAL ATTACK
25 Sept. – 11 Nov., 1918

⌐⌐⌐⌐⌐   HINDENBURG LINE
Other trench systems not indicated

••••••••••••   ST. QUENTIN CANAL.

25 miles

Map No. 19

ST. - MIHIEL

SWITZERLAND
100 miles

telephones, power plants, hospitals, and even stables. Some of the soldiers lived on barges floating in this underground passageway. So that they could dash to their trenches and help the lookouts fight, they had underground stairways. These were unknown to the soldiers of the 27th and 30th American Divisions who were to smash through the line at this point.

Haig's fierce fight was known as the "Somme Offensive of 1918." It started in late September with the Allied artillery pounding the German trenches, drenching them with mustard gas. Although the pincers on the map curve behind the enemy in simple-looking arcs, this was hard fighting. It was over the ground on which so many Allied soldiers had given their lives two years before.

The 27th Division, nicknamed "The New York Division" because its men were from the Empire State, moved forward with tanks helping them. But murderous fire from two farms which the Germans had fortified, and from the Knoll, forced part of the division back. In the leading regiment, of ninety-four young company officers, ninety-two were killed or wounded. Confusion resulted.

But the fighting New Yorkers overran the crest of the ridge and pushed on without stopping to "mop up." Germans streamed out of a hidden passageway and fired into the backs of the front wave and into reserves coming up. Australians came to the rescue of the New Yorkers.

There was bravery, too, in the 30th Infantry Division. The soldiers called it "Old Hickory Division," because its men were from Tennessee, North and South Carolina. The man the South Carolinians talked about after the campaign was not a fighter, but a stretcher bearer, Homer E. Bryant, of Salem, South Carolina.

Bryant's company was stopped behind a hill. From just over the top came cries of "Help! My God, help!" Homer Bryant got ready to cross over the crest. "Don't go!" a man warned. "They have sniper and machine-gun fire up there. You'll be killed."

A burst of fire in front of the rolling hill ripped out a warning. Private Bryant ran his hand across his brow. It was damp with sweat. He buckled his dish-shaped helmet tighter. "I have to go," he said. "It might be one of our guys."

The men tried to stop him, but Bryant rushed over the hill to the wounded man. When he ran down the slope, machine-gun fire killed him.

Months later, Bryant's father received the Distinguished Service Cross for his son. One of the great tragedies of war is the loss of men on both sides like Stretcher Bearer Homer E. Bryant.

Not all the bravery was on the ground. To help American infantrymen go forward across No Man's Land in the face of German guns, First Lieutenant Louis Bernheimer, of New York City, was ordered to fly his observation plane, a DH-4, over the German trenches to make photographs. With him as cameraman-gunner was young Second Lieutenant John W. Jordan, of Indianapolis. If the photos could be taken at a low altitude, they would disclose to the infantrymen the location of the guns.

Protecting the DH-4, which could fly at only 125 miles per hour, were three pursuit planes. Their top speed was about the same as the DH-4.

No sooner was John Jordan taking pictures than the American formation was attacked by twelve German Fokkers. Bernheimer did not get excited. He knew that his friend, Second Lieutenant James S. D. Burns, also of New York City, was above him furnishing protection. Bernheimer kept his ship steady so that Jordan could take his photos. Bullets smacked through the ship and struck Jordan in the shoulder and leg. Although he was in pain, John Jordan had the nerve and grit to keep operating his camera.

The Fokkers whirred closer, determined to down the Americans. Burns was shot through the heart. He fell across the controls. His pilot, Second Lieutenant Roger W. Hitchcock of Los Angeles, struggled to lift Burns's body from the wires. Their plane tumbled 8,000 feet. Hitchcock tugged at the body of the dead gunner and fought to stay in his plane. When his ship was almost on the ground, Hitchcock righted it and flew his dead friend back to the airdrome.

While Hitchcock's plane was falling, Joel H. McClendon of Ferris, Texas, a first lieutenant piloting a pursuit plane in rear of the American observation ship, saw five Fokkers attack Bernheimer. McClendon could see Jordan, wounded, trying to fight off the enemy planes with his machine guns. McClendon turned in his seat and shouted at his gunner-observer, Second Lieutenant Charles W. Plummer of New Bedford, Massachusetts. The roar of the motor drowned the sound of the words. Plummer did not have to hear the message, for the Texan flew him into the heart of the German formation. Plummer stood up. The wind rushed at him. The wires of the plane screamed. He pressed the trigger of his machine guns, sending a stream of bullets into the German planes.

The Fokkers forgot the photographic plane. They zoomed up, turned over, and then plunged down on graceful arcs. In a few moments they sprayed McClendon's plane with bullets. It caught fire, stalled, then fell like a stone, carrying McClendon and Plummer to their deaths.

The other American pilot, First Lieutenant Philip R. Babcock of Lynn, Massachusetts, with his gunner, Second Lieutenant Joseph A. Palmer of Zanesville, Ohio, fought to drive the Fokkers away from Bernheimer's observation plane, and they were successful.

But while Bernheimer was piloting his ship home the Fokkers whirred back after him. Jordan put his camera down. For the second time he forgot his wounds. He sent machine-gun bullets at the German planes and enabled his pilot to land safely. At the airdrome, Lieutenant Bernheimer taxied to a stop. Mechanics and Bernheimer helped John Jordan out of his seat. His films were developed quickly, and shortly a motorcycle messenger sped to the infantry with thirty-six photographs obtained at fearful cost.

The Distinguished Service Cross for extraordinary heroism was awarded Bernheimer, Jordan, Babcock, Palmer, and Hitchcock.

Mr. James Burns, Mr. Henry Plummer, and Mr. J. W. McClendon received the same medal with its blue, red and white trimmed ribbon—but for their sons. Seldom in the history of aerial combat has there been greater determination than that shown by these four pilots and their gunners.

Brave deeds and more hard fighting by the Allies along the long battle line sent the Germans into retreat. The British attacks along the northern pincer won success. Soon bad weather slowed the attackers, yet large numbers of Germans were captured.

Ludendorff, the great general, saw that the war was hopeless and resigned. Hindenburg sent the Kaiser a message telling him that the fighting must stop. *Every day of delay,* Hindenburg wrote to the Kaiser, *costs thousands of brave soldiers their lives.*

The Kaiser was shocked. Worse news for him came from Kiel. The leaders of his Grand Fleet ordered it to sea, but the sailors and marines refused to man the ships. Four years of inaction had sapped their nerve. (The best sailors had been drafted into the submarine service.) The sailors saw no use in more fighting. They shouted, "Down with the Kaiser!"

When the Kaiser heard of the mutiny of his navy he cried, "Treason! Shameless treason!" He could not bring himself to believe that the war was over, that the German nation was defeated. In a message to his people he wrote, ... *Whether arms must be lowered is a question.... We must stand our ground against our enemies.... The hour is grave.... I will only extend my hand for an honorable peace.*

But the Germans had had enough of the Kaiser. They were having a hard time getting food. Revolution broke out. It was headed by Dr. Karl Liebknecht, a Communist who had once been the leader of the German Socialist Party. He published an article calling for the workers in the ammunition factories to stop and for the soldiers to disarm their officers, and he also asked for the Kaiser's death.

The German people had fought bravely and with endurance. Now they were beaten. Austria asked for peace on any terms.

On November 10, 1918, at five in the morning, the Kaiser

and a small group of aides made an escape to Holland on a special train. The Kaiser lived with the Dutch for many years. He was a sad figure. During the war he had scarcely governed his country. He let others control it. The Kaiser's son, the Crown Prince, refused to flee to Holland. He led his army back home.

In a railway coach parked on a siding in the forest of Compiègne in north-central France, fifty miles from Paris, German envoys met to hear the conditions of the Allies for an armistice. Marshal Foch, now a stern figure, dominated the scene. At five o'clock in the morning of November 11, 1918, the long-looked-for Armistice was signed. The war was over.

There was a strange silence at the front. The land, a long zigzag width of it extending from the sea in Belgium to the Swiss border, was wrecked. But greater wrecks were made of people's lives. Millions of families lost their fathers, a loss that could not be replaced.

When they heard of the Armistice, the soldiers at the front did not celebrate. They marched out of their stinking trenches with silent prayers of thanksgiving. They oiled their weapons, praying they were through using them. In Paris, as in other leading cities of the Allies, there were wild celebrations. Twelve hundred guns were fired in salute. The bells rang in every church, and crowds filled the streets. General Pershing wrote in his book, *My Experiences in the World War:*

... Everybody was still celebrating when I arrived in Paris [the afternoon the Armistice was signed]. It looked as though the whole population had gone out of their minds. The boulevards were packed with people wearing all sorts of odd costumes. The crowds were doing clownish things.... It was bedlam.

In the old cathedral city of Chartres, France, the band played "La Marseillaise" over and over again. Then the populace marched to the cemetery to honor the dead.

In churches all over the world bells rang and people went to church and thanked God that the war had ended. More than

12,000,000 people had been killed, wounded, or were missing, or had died of disease or starvation. Thousands had no homes.

The people of the world looked forward to a lasting peace. President Wilson's phrase, "A war to make the world safe for democracy," gave them the hope that the four years of war just over would end all wars.

The terms of the Armistice were hard on the Germans, but probably not as harsh as the Germans would have levied had they been the victors. Under the terms of the Armistice, the German armies had to withdraw to their own soil. They had to agree to let the Allies send armies to German territory. The Germans were required to surrender all submarines and most of their other implements of war, such as artillery, planes, and machine guns. The Germans were forced to give the Allies many trucks and railroad cars. The principal battleships of the German fleet, with cruisers and destroyers, were delivered to the Allies.

President Wilson outlined Fourteen Points, which he said were necessary so the world could enjoy peace forever. He arranged for the United States to send great quantities of food to starving peoples in the Balkans, to needy Belgians, and to the people of northern France. The populace of Europe began to look upon Woodrow Wilson as their future savior.

But when the President went to Paris for the Peace Conference, he entered into bitter arguments with Clemenceau, Lloyd George, and Orlando, the Premier of Italy. Wilson told everyone that a League of Nations would bring permanent peace. He worked hard to establish the League, and it broke his heart when the majority of the people of the United States would not support it.

But all the fighting did not end with the Armistice. In Russia, Allied soldiers, including Americans, fought on. And as smart a leader as President Wilson was, he could not make up his mind what to do about it.

Chapter 31

THE DEVIL ON ICE SKATES

A HUSKY major general sat in a private room in the Kansas City railroad station. Through the walls came the labored throb of an engine. The general's own pulse thumped as he listened to the small man sitting opposite him, Secretary of War Newton D. Baker.

General Graves leaned back and tugged nervously at his thick brown mustache. His rimless spectacles, the "stand-up" collar of his uniform, and his rather prim manner made William S. Graves look more like the principal of a school than a two-star general. His eyes widened as he listened to Mr. Baker.

"General Graves," the Secretary said, "some time I'll tell you why you have to go to Siberia. If you want to cuss out anyone for sending you, I'm the man to cuss."

Newton D. Baker stood up. So did the general, and he towered over Mr. Baker. The Secretary of War handed Graves a red-bordered envelope. "I'm sorry I'm in such a rush," Baker said. "In this envelope is the policy you are to follow. My advice: *watch your step.* You'll be walking on eggs loaded with dynamite. Good-by, and God bless you."

This was a weird beginning to a weird, confusing adventure. When Graves was alone he studied the orders in the queer-looking envelope. They were dated July 17, 1918, and they bore the heading *Aide Memoire*.

In the next nineteen months, in Siberia, the American general, Graves, would study the *aide memoire* countless times. It

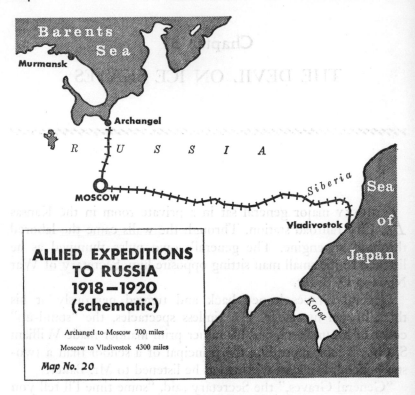

**ALLIED EXPEDITIONS
TO RUSSIA
1918–1920
(schematic)**

Archangel to Moscow 700 miles

Moscow to Vladivostok 4300 miles

Map No. 20

did not explain why he was ordered to that cold land, and General Graves did not ask. Nor did he inquire in the future.

When General Graves arrived in Siberia he found that the *aide memoire* did not match the situation. But Graves was a soldier, and he decided that the strange document was something to be carried out to the letter.

The world was in "baffling disorder," Mr. Baker had said. After arriving at Vladivostok, Siberia, Graves believed it.

General Graves's mission to Siberia was complicated. His job was as mixed up as a kettle of eels. He had made a list of the key points of the *aide memoire:*

The United States wants to win the war against Germany. To do this the United States must co-operate with its Allies. Our country has no selfish desires for territory nor thirst for power. To win, we must send large numbers of men to France. We cannot afford to send great numbers of soldiers elsewhere.

There is tragic confusion in Russia. The only fighting the United States can do there is to help a large force of Czech soldiers (deserters and prisoners from the Austrian Army, who have joined the Czar's Army) fight their way out of Russia. The Czech soldiers are trying to get out by means of the Trans-Siberian Railway.

Our soldiers in Vladivostok must guard supplies there which may be needed by the Russians.

If the Russians want us to help them, we must do so. The United States must not restrict the policies of its Allies. We are not to interfere with Russian politics or Russian affairs, and we will ask our Allies to do the same. We want the Russians to control their own destiny.

Our soldiers in Siberia must keep close co-operation with the small military force from Japan.

As soon as possible, in order to help the Russians, the United States hopes to send to Siberia a team of merchants, agricultural experts, labor advisors, Red Cross men, and men from the Y.M.C.A.

General Graves scratched his head. The *aide memoire* had more points than the orders for the cadet guards in barracks when the general was a West Point cadet. Later, Graves received a letter from the Chief of Staff of the Army, Peyton C. March, four-star general. March wrote, "Keep a stiff upper lip, Graves. I am going to stand by you until Hell freezes over." March did not desert his friend, but for most of the time Graves was in Russia it seemed to him that the Devil was on ice skates.

The mission was difficult and there was little guidance from anyone.

To help accomplish his task, General Graves had 5,000 soldiers from Camp Fremont, California, and 2,500 more from the Philippines.

When he arrived in Vladivostok, a port on the Sea of Japan, Graves found the situation even more confusing than the *aide memoire*. The port was a topsy-turvy mess. There was no port control, and mountains of supplies were scattered over acres of ground. These war supplies were worth $750,000,000 in 1918 currency. They had been sent by the Allies, principally by the United States, to help the Russians fight the Germans.

There were piles and piles of supplies. The hills around the city were covered with them. There were so many crates, bags, and boxes, that Mr. George Kennan, in writing of them, said that if they were shipped at the rate of forty carloads a day it would take between three and four years to move them all. There were at least one thousand automobiles in crates. The Czar's armies could have used these supplies, but the Russian supply officers and Russian railways had been too inefficient to get them to the front. And now the Russians were no longer fighting the Germans.

Wild rumors flew about the port. It was said that an army of Bolsheviki was coming to seize the supplies. Other rumors said that the Germans themselves were coming to seize them.

The *aide memoire* given to General Graves talked of a "small" Japanese force. The general found 72,000 Japanese soldiers at Vladivostok, and there were 12,000 more bothering the Chinese in China. More Japanese soldiers were arriving. The Japanese had broken their word in sending a force many times larger than they had promised. Obviously, they were after territory.

The general took a look at the mountains of supplies and saw that tons and tons of them were there for the taking. He placed his men on guard about them while he investigated. He discovered that confusion was everywhere. The English, French, and Japanese were working to fight bolshevism and they expected Graves to join hands. The Bolsheviki were the enemies of the Czar. But the *aide memoire* said that we must not interfere with Russian affairs and that we must ask our Allies not to do so.

When General Graves refused to fight the Bolsheviki, the Allies became angry.

One of the questions the general had to face was what to do about the Russian Admiral Alexandria Kolchak. Kolchak was "a character," a Russian patriot who was determined to fight the Bolsheviki. When the Russian Revolution started, this dramatic admiral commanded the Russian Black Sea Fleet. When his Russian sailors mutinied, they demanded his sword, but Kolchak threw it overboard to indicate that he would never surrender. Later, in Siberia, this fiery sailor wanted to be a military dictator. He was a problem, and his staff was an even greater one, for they were the worst type of Czarist officers.

The people of Siberia were in a terrible nutcracker. Admiral Kolchak was determined to fight Communism, and to do it he raided Siberian villages for men for his army. His methods were so harsh he turned Russians toward Communism as the lesser of two evils. For example, if the admiral received no co-operation from a village, he had its leaders hauled out and whipped, or shot, or dipped into the waters of an icy lake until they became icicles. If he found a man hiding from his recruiters, the man faced death by torture.

Almost as bad a scourge as Kolchak and his lieutenants were the wild Cossacks and the Bolsheviki. They plundered and burned. The more defenseless the town, the "braver" the Cossacks.

The country was drenched in blood. On one occasion, a bandit named Gregory Semenoff massacred fifty-two carloads of men, women, and children—Siberian peasants—by turning machine guns on them. It was hard to know which side Semenoff was on.

While Admiral Kolchak was ravaging the country, he became angry at General Graves and complained to the United States' State Department that the general was "un-co-operative." This amounted to little, but it irritated Graves.

Kolchak finally was beaten. When the Reds captured him they placed him before a firing squad and shot out his brains. Kolchak's death signaled the end of the White counterrevolution against the Siberian Soviets.

But the admiral's execution did not end the problems confronting General Graves. For instance, in the *aide memoire* was the directive to help the Czechs out of Russia and back to their homeland. To complicate a confusing picture, the British cancelled ships that would transport the Czechs away from Russia. There were no plans for more ships.

The Czechs were men of real combat value. Three thousand were in Vladivostok, and 62,000 were scattered along the Trans-Siberian railroad, far into the interior of Russia. They wanted to get home. They could only do this if they obtained control of the railroad.

In order to control the long stretch of railroad, the Czechs were moving along the railroad in armored trains. They were assisted at times by the "White Russians" (more correctly known as the "Whites") who were anti-Bolsheviki. The magic word "home," and all it stands for, caused the Czechs to fight the Bolsheviki.

In order to help the Czech soldiers, some of General Graves's Americans penetrated into the interior of Russia, along the railroad, as far as 1,400 miles from Vladivostok, where they had fights with the Communists. In one of these fights Major Robert L. Eichelberger, of Ohio, who was working to gather information, was cut off from Vladivostok. It was several weeks before this young major could get back. Twenty-five years later he became a four-star general and helped General MacArthur win his campaign against the Japanese.

The confusing situation in Vladivostok became worse when an election was held there. The results of this election disclosed that the majority of the Russians in the seaport were Communists. This was the crowning blow. It was hard for General Graves to know what to do. The Allies decided not to let the Vladivostok Bolsheviki control the city.

When the news of the Armistice reached Vladivostok, Graves and his soldiers were happy. There was excitement. Rumors about going home were on almost every tongue. "There is no excuse for us to remain in Russia now," the soldiers said. But months passed and nothing happened. President Wilson could not make up his mind what to do with General Graves and his soldiers. Graves and his men in Siberia felt marooned. They became bitter.

Allied ships sailed in and hauled away the mountains of supplies. Most of the Czechs finally arrived in Vladivostok and were shipped home.

The Japanese were not as anxious to leave as were the Americans, for the Japanese had their eyes on territory. They fought the Russians in eastern Siberia. Four years later peace conferences finally forced the Japanese out of Russia.

The snow-covered country of Siberia, with its knifelike winds, was as desolate as the hopes of Graves and his Americans.

Graves wrote that he did not even know what the United States was trying to accomplish by sending a force to Siberia. The Americans disliked being in Russia, and the Russians hated having Allied soldiers there. General Graves, in his book *America's Siberian Adventure*, wrote that keeping our soldiers and other Allied soldiers in Siberia resulted in great numbers of Russians becoming solidly behind the Soviets.

Forty-one years later, when Khrushchev, the Russian premier, spoke in Los Angeles, he talked of how Americans must remember that they fought Russians on Russian soil. He employed the Communist custom of conveniently glossing over facts. He did not mention that the supplies the Allied soldiers were guarding belonged to the Allies, that the Russians were stealing them, and that as soon as the Communist party came into power it declared war on all "capitalist" countries. The Communists were happy to kill Allied soldiers.

Finally, on April 1, 1920, sixteen months after the Armistice, the all-but-forgotten group of United States soldiers sailed for home.

Chapter 32

THE POLAR BEARS

THE story of the Allies in northern Russia parallels the experiences of the Allies in Vladivostok.[1] Both are sad tales. Soon after the fall of the Czar, the Allied governments talked of sending soldiers to north Russia. They hoped it would reopen the Eastern Front. If it would, Germany would be handicapped, and would once again have to fight in two widely separated areas. The Allies had sent large quantities of supplies to north Russia—lead, aluminum, copper, weapons, ammunition, and many other military supplies. Now that the Czar's armies had collapsed, these supplies were in danger of being taken by the Communists, like the supplies in Vladivostok. The question of guarding the supplies came up.

President Wilson shook his head. He did not like the idea of sending American soldiers to Russia. "That is interference in Russian affairs," he said. This was 1918, and he could see that every available soldier was needed in France; that was where the war would be won or lost.

France and Britain decided to send soldiers to north Russia, but there were problems. The situation was almost as mixed up as affairs in Siberia. The "Whites" were trying to rally their forces and seize the country. They hated the Bolsheviki. The Bolsheviki made it clear they did not want Allied soldiers in the country. If they came, they said, they would fight. Next, there

[1] See Map No. 20, page 214.

was the difficulty of weather. The two ports in the dreary country, Murmansk and Archangel, through which troops and supplies would pass, were icebound half the year. Soldiers fighting in arctic temperatures should have special clothing and training.

To complicate a confusing situation even more, the people in north Russia, about 50,000 of them, were about to starve. The peasants eked a living from the barren ground by growing a few crops in the short, hot summer. But trainloads of refugees were pouring in from the interior of Russia to escape the terrorism of the Bolsheviki. There was not enough food to go around.

The two port cities were dirty and primitive. A Russian, Admiral Kyetlinski, who was forceful as well as fair, kept order. But Kyetlinski was murdered. Immediately, Communist agitators moved in and preached "riot." Their targets were the Russian sailors of the Czar's Navy, who were out of work. Gangs roamed the streets. Some of the citizens sent word to the Allies asking for protection.

The British and the French were far more decisive about trying to solve these problems than the Americans. They sent an expedition to north Russia under the command of a pleasant Englishman, Brigadier F. C. Poole. Shortly, British and French warships guarding the transports sailed into Murmansk harbor. It was April, 1918.

The American ambassador to Russia, Mr. David R. Francis, sent cablegrams to Washington begging that United States soldiers be sent to Russia, and his messages added to the pressure on the President. Mr. Francis saw the future clearly. He called Communism "a foul monster."

President Wilson was in a quandary. In his own words, he "sweat blood" over the problem. He finally wrote, *Military intervention in Russia will only add to the confusion. It will not help win the war against Germany.*

The British and French force in north Russia totaled only 1,500 men. Mr. Wilson thought of how in 1812 the immense country, Russia, had swallowed Napoleon's Grand Army. The United States could not send a huge force to Russia. What good,

Wilson reasoned, could a few troops do in north Russia except guard the supplies? And he felt—strongly—that the United States should not meddle in the internal affairs of another country.

But after long days of wrestling with the problem and himself, President Wilson ordered the United States warship *Olympia* and about 4,500 United States soldiers to Russia. They arrived ninety days after the French and British.

The Americans ordered to north Russia were from Michigan and Wisconsin, members of the 339th Infantry Regiment. When they saw the desolate land they must have wondered what sins they had committed. It was August. Already chilly winds were sweeping in from the sea. It was cold enough for the soldiers to discover that the hobnails in the soles of their shoes would have to be removed, because they made the feet of the wearers so cold.

When the soldiers arrived, many were ill from influenza. There was no hospital for them to go to, so they stayed aboard in the leaky, foul-smelling holds of the transports.

The American soldiers were not told *why* they were in Russia. Just before the troops arrived, Mr. Francis had received a cable from Washington: AMERICAN TROOPS WILL BE EMPLOYED ONLY TO GUARD MILITARY SUPPLIES. Francis was disappointed. He knew the force available was small, but he wanted to do everything possible to smash the growing evil, Communism.

But in a few days American sailors were fighting the Communists. This came about in a peculiar way. The *Olympia* had arrived at Archangel a month ahead of the American troop transports. Soon after the ship dropped anchor there was a check aboard the vessel to find out who the best rifle shots were. Fifty bluejackets were selected. They were put ashore and were rushed to help an expedition that was battling Communists. The leader was Brigadier Poole. The first thing the young American sailors knew, they were walking down the railroad track toward Moscow. They were recalled, but not before they had been in battle against the Communists.

When the American soldiers arrived, their colonel carried

out his instructions and reported to Brigadier Poole. Poole ordered them to join a force marching down the railroad track for the interior of Russia. The railroad was the avenue of attack, and it stretched ahead for seemingly endless distances.

The American soldiers, while brave, were not well-trained. Some had not even targeted their rifles; they had little confidence in their weapons. They had to learn on the job, which is a poor method when the task involves fighting. Neither did they have the advantage of having a colonel along with them. Their colonel believed that his place was back in headquarters in Archangel.

Many of the men from Michigan and Wisconsin were factory workers, unacquainted with outdoor life—particularly in a world where the weather pushed the mercury in the thermometer down out of sight. Before long, the ground froze to a depth of six feet. Blizzards lashed the countryside. Fortunately, friends close by helped. These were soldiers in the British force from Canada.

A ray of hope appeared when Britain sent a fine leader, Field Marshal Lord Ironside. The Allies were happy to have him command the force. Ironside, a huge man, was placid, smart, experienced, and forceful. The French soldiers called him *"le magnifique géant."*

Ironside slowed down the advance. Proceeding into the immense country with a small force of 9,500 seemed foolhardy. And the Russian winter was at hand.

When the winter snows came, the Allied soldiers chopped down trees and built log cabins. Living in the gloomy forests was trying. The weather became so cold that when wood had to be brought in the men went out in pairs; if one man went alone and slipped, spraining his ankle, or if any other accident occurred, he would freeze to death. Patrols were sent out on snowshoes and skis, and the men experienced thirst on the snow trail. There was nothing for the soldiers to do when they were off duty. Scattered about the vast country were a few Russian villages. The Russian peasants were friendly but stolid. In their off time, the Allied soldiers followed the example of the peasants—they sat by the fires and waited for spring. Fortunately, the soldiers had fur clothing: hats, gloves, and coats.

Once in a while Communist patrols snowshoed through the forest and attacked the sentries. This was almost a relief, because it was excitement. When this happened, the soldiers in the cabins struggled into their heavy clothing, grabbed their rifles, and dashed out to help the sentries. In every such raid, the Communists faded back quickly into the forest as soon as the firing line against them was operating.

Suddenly there came unbelievably joyous news: THE WAR IS OVER. AN ARMISTICE HAS BEEN SIGNED IN FRANCE. The soldiers' morale skyrocketed. They were deliriously happy. Friends hugged one another. They wondered how soon ships could arrive in Archangel to transport them home.

Then, just as suddenly, heartbreaking orders flashed from Washington: THE SIGNING OF THE ARMISTICE HAS CREATED NO CHANGE IN YOUR SITUATION. The soldiers could not believe it. They said to one another, "We haven't declared war on Russia. Why are we here?"

The winter dragged on. There was discomfort, dirt, boredom, and rumors. When a Communist patrol killed a sentry it now seemed doubly ghastly. The dead man was a battle casualty, yet the Armistice had been signed ending the war.

When spring finally arrived, billions of mosquitoes flew out of the swamps. This was a new torment. The American quartermasters had not foreseen this, and the soldiers suffered for want of mosquito nets, head nets, and gloves. The only refuge from the swarms of insects was a choking, smoky fire.

Most of the fights with the Communists, except for a fierce battle which the British fought near Murmansk, were small. But when you face even one enemy soldier and bullets come at you, it seems as dangerous as if you were in a battle. The soldiers were under pressure. Their morale sank lower and lower. Letters arrived from home asking, *Why don't they send you back to the States? The war is over.*

The United States soldiers felt forgotten by their country.

The French soldiers talked of mutiny. The British had the best leadership, and they set the example for the soldiers of the other nations. Congressmen from Michigan and Wisconsin tried to make President Wilson order the soldiers home, but Mr. Wilson was having as hard a time making up his mind what to do now as he had when he wrestled with the problem of sending the soldiers to Russia in the first place.

Finally, in August, 1919, nine months after the Armistice was signed, the Americans in north Russia sailed for home. Soon, the other Allies sailed for their homes.

The Americans who served in north Russia felt badly about leaving their dead in the tundra and forests. Some had been buried in the snow and ice. Eventually, many of the bodies were recovered and reburied in the United States, many of them in the White Chapel Cemetery near Detroit. The dominating emblem on the monument watching over these American dead is a polar bear.

Chapter 33

LOOKING BACK

THE chief lesson learned from the war was one of co-operation. Nations saw that to survive they must have strong allies. However, this lesson was not obvious to every nation at first.

After 1914 it became apparent to every nation except the United States that a great power cannot ignore its military forces. Most nations learned that if a country has weak military strength it is difficult to have successful diplomacy. The United States finally learned this lesson just prior to the Second World War.

The best way to keep war away is to be prepared for it, and to employ civil leaders who are smart, devoted, and far-seeing.

The First World War changed life. The casualties and the wrecked homes brought sorrow to millions of families. It is hard to determine the number killed in action and the number who died of wounds. The following is an estimate of men killed:

Germany	3,000,000
Russia	3,000,000
France	1,400,000
British Empire	1,000,000
Austria-Hungary	1,000,000
Italy	500,000
United States	81,000
Turkey	No records

The Russian figure is a guess. The total death toll, including civilian deaths from war accidents, disease, and starvation, is estimated to be from 12,000,000 to 15,000,000.

In the First World War, Russia demonstrated what happens when rulers set their will above the people.

Japan entered the war on the Allied side but resisted every plea that she send soldiers to France. Instead, the Japanese seized a German base on the coast of China. Japan's thirst for power was exposed—and overlooked. She also grabbed German-owned islands in the South Pacific and kept them.

Germany started the war and lost it. Her soldiers and officers fought bravely and with skill. Germany was handicapped by weak allies.

Poison gas, tanks, and planes were introduced in war for the first time.

In the Second World War, Marshal Henri P. Pétain sullied the wonderful reputation he acquired as a leader in the First World War by helping the Nazis of Germany after they had overrun his country. He was tried for treason and sentenced to death. His former lieutenant, General de Gaulle, changed the sentence of the court to life imprisonment.

In World War I the United States played the decisive role. The Americans suffered far fewer casualties than their allies. The Allies could not have won but for the effort of the United States.

ACKNOWLEDGMENTS

Mr. Kenneth Roberts, author, once wrote, *Every writer needs a friend who will listen with patient understanding and who will point out errors and will help*. Two such invaluable souls interested themselves in this book: my wife, Dort Darrah Reeder, and Lieutenant Colonel John R. Elting of the West Point faculty. Dort Reeder typed and retyped this manuscript, and typed it again. She accompanied me to Europe, acted as interpreter, woke up sleepy guards in museums, turned on museum lights, and took notes. She searched guidebooks to discover places we might go to obtain information. And, not least, she encouraged me, and understood when I shut myself up to devote time to this story. Colonel Elting is a historian whose hobby is history. He steered me away from sources carelessly and inaccurately written. He corrected the manuscript. It gained from his wealth of knowledge and from his store of historical anecdotes. Colonel Elting's ability to relate anecdotes is a characteristic that makes him a favorite lecturer of the West Point cadets.

I thank Colonel Vincent J. ("Mike") Esposito, soldier, author, and professor, for use of material from his *West Point Atlas of American Wars, volume II*. Many of the maps in this book are based upon maps in his *Atlas*.

John Kieran, who fought in World War I and who rose to world-wide fame as a writer, naturalist, and radio and television star, interested himself in the part of this book that describes an action in which his regiment, the 11th Engineers, fought.

Colonel E. R. (Wort) Williams helped me in unusual ways at the Meuse-Argonne and Verdun battlefields. Lieutenant Armel Michel, of the French Army, assisted by escorting me on the ground at Verdun.

Mr. Reinhard Pradel, interpreter and information specialist in Headquarters, Seventh United States Army in Europe, worked to obtain for me stories of heroism and of combat from the archives of the Library of Contemporary History in Stuttgart, Germany.

Mr. Morris Honick, Historical Branch, Supreme Headquarters Allied Powers Europe, secured the co-operation of the *Ministre de la Guerre* in Paris. As a result of their work, this book contains a number of anecdotes of World War I fighters.

General Robert L. Eichelberger contributed to this book by describing, a year before his death, his experiences in Siberia, where he served as a young combat leader and as an intelligence officer.

Part of the chorus to "Over There" by George M. Cohan is used by permission. Copyright 1917/Copyright Renewal 1945 Leo Feist, Inc., N. Y., N. Y.

The diagram in Chapter 18 showing Allied shipping losses in April, 1917 is reproduced with the permission of Charles Scribner's Sons from *Military History of the World War* (page 376) by Girard L. McEntee (copyright 1937 by Charles Scribner's Sons).

I am also indebted to *The New York Times* for permission and assistance in reproducing part of a front page of the *Times* announcing the United States declaration of war.

On every single occasion on which I have asked the staff of the United States Military Academy Library for support I have received maximum co-operation. The following members of the library staff became interested in the problems pertaining to this work and helped by assembling books and manuscripts: Miss Thelma Bedell, Mr. John B. Tucker, Mrs. Frank Mattola, Miss Irene Feith, Miss Anne Pierce, and Mr. William Kerr. I appreciated their skilled assistance.

I thank the United States Army for the use of three photographs.

I also desire to thank the following, who either contributed information or assisted in gathering it: Lt. Col. Mark M. Boatner III, Lieutenant General Blackshear M. Bryan, Mr. Tim Cohane, Mr. Hermann Deutsch, Mr. Charles Hawkins, First Lieutenant Dale E. Hruby, Colonel Kenneth E. Lay, Mr. Frank Lorson, Colonel E. W. Richardson, Colonel Charles P. Summerall, Jr., and Doctor Theodore C. Speers. Mr. Kenneth Roberts is correct: *An author may have enthusiasm, but to complete his work he must have helpful friends.*

The following individuals were also kind and contributed in one or more ways. I thank them for their help. Mrs. Gerda L. Freeman, Lieutenant Colonel C. J. George, Colonel F. Z. Kovach, Mr. Joseph Pascale, Major R. F. Prentiss, Major John A. Santoro, Major James F. Sunderman, Honorable Harry S. Truman, and Mr. Richard Ullman.

RED REEDER

West Point
New York

AUTHORITIES CONSULTED

In the study of this war I referred to many books. The principal ones are listed here. The books marked * were special guideposts.

American Armies and Battlefields in Europe. Prepared by the U. S. American Battle Monuments Commission. Washington, D. C.: U. S. Government Printing Office, 1938.

Barnes, Major R. Money, *The Uniforms and History of the Scottish Regiments.* London: Seeley Service & Co., 1956.

Boughton, VanTuyl, *History of the Eleventh Engineers United States Army.* New York: J. J. Little and Ives Co., 1927.

Churchill, Winston, *Great Contemporaries.* New York: G. P. Putnam's Sons, 1937.

Clark, Stanley Frederick, *The Man Who Is France.* New York: Dodd, Mead & Co., 1960.

Cramer, C. H., *Newton D. Baker.* New York: The World Publishing Co., 1961.

Cruttwell, Charles R. M., *A History of the Great War, 1914–1918.* Oxford: The Clarendon Press, 1934.

Cudahy, John, *Archangel.* Chicago: A. C. McClurg & Co., 1924.

D'Arnoux, Jacques, *Les Sept Colonnes de L'héroisme.* Paris: Librairie Plon, 1938.

de Chambrun, Colonel Jacques and de Marenches, Captain Charles, *The American Army in the European Conflict.* New York: The Macmillan Co., 1919.

De Weerd, Harvey A., *Great Soldiers of the Two World Wars.* New York: W. W. Norton & Co., 1941.

Dickman, Joseph T., Major General, *The Great Crusade*. New York: D. Appleton and Co., 1927.

Driggs, Laurence La Tourette, *Heroes of Aviation*. Boston: Little, Brown and Co., 1918.

DuPuy, R. Ernest, *Men of West Point*. New York: William Sloane Associates, 1951.

*———*Perish by the Sword*. Harrisburg, Penna.: The Military Service Publishing Co., 1939.

*Esposito, Colonel Vincent J., *The West Point Atlas of American Wars*, vol. II. New York: Frederick A. Praeger, 1955.

*Falls, Cyril, *The Great War*, New York: G. P. Putnam's Sons, 1959.

Flick, Ella M. E., *Chaplain Duffy*. Philadelphia: The Dolphin Press, 1935.

Foerster, Wolfgang, and Greiner, Helmuth (editors), *Wir Kämpfer im Weltkrieg 1914–1918*. Berlin: F. W. Peters Verlag.

French, Field Marshal Viscount of Ypres, *1914*. Boston: Houghton Mifflin Co., 1919.

Frothingham, Thomas G., *The Naval History of the World War*. Cambridge: Harvard University Press, 1926.

Fuller, J. F. C., Major General, *A Military History of the Western World*, vol. 3; New York: Funk & Wagnalls Co., 1956.

——— *Memoirs of an Unconventional Soldier*. London: Ivor Nicholson and Watson, Ltd., 1936.

Gourko, Basil, General, *War and Revolution in Russia 1914–1917*. New York: The Macmillan Co., 1919.

Graves, William S., *America's Siberian Adventure, 1918–1920*. New York: Jonathan Cape and Harrison Smith, 1931.

Halliday, E. M., *The Ignorant Armies*. New York: Harper and Brothers, 1958.

Harbord, James Guthrie, *The American Army in France 1917–1918*. Boston: Little, Brown and Co., 1936.

Hemenway, Frederic V., *History of the Third Division, United States Army in the World War*. Andernach-On-The-Rhine: 1919.

History of the First Division. Philadelphia: The John C. Winston Co., 1922.

History of the 316th Field Artillery, 2nd Lt. Alexander C. Stevens, ed. Chicago: Rogers and Hall Co. (no date).

Hoehling, A. A., *The Fierce Lambs*. Boston: Little, Brown and Co., 1960.

Horne, Charles F., *Source Records of the Great War*. National Alumni, 1923.

Infantry in Battle. Washington, D. C.: The Infantry Journal, Inc., 1939.

Insignia and Decorations of the U. S. Armed Forces. ("*Traditions and Glamour of Insignia*" by Arthur E. DuBois). Washington, D. C.: National Geographic Society, 1944.

Ironside, Edmund, Major General Sir, *Tannenberg*. Edinburgh: William Blackwood & Sons, 1925.

Jacobs, Bruce, *Heroes of The Army*. New York: W. W. Norton and Co., Inc., 1956.

Johnson, Thomas M. and Pratt, Fletcher, *The Lost Battalion*. New York: The Bobbs-Merrill Co., 1938.

*Kennan, George F., *The Decision to Intervene*. Princeton, N. J.: Princeton University Press, 1958.

Knox, Alfred, Major General Sir, *With The Russian Army 1914–1917*, 2 vols. New York: E. P. Dutton & Co., 1921.

Lamberton, W. H. (compiler) and Cheesman, E. F. (editor), *Fighter Aircraft of the 1914–1918 War*. England: Letchworth, Herts.: Harleyford Publications, 1960.

Lawrence, Thomas E., *Revolt in the Desert*. New York: George H. Doran Co., 1927.

Lehmann, Captain Ernst and Mingos, Howard, *The Zeppelins*. New York: J. H. Sears & Co., Inc., 1927.

Liddell Hart, Basil Henry, *Reputations Ten Years After*. Boston: Little, Brown and Co., 1928.

——— *The Tanks*. New York: Frederick A. Praeger, 1959.

Metcalf, Clyde Hill, Lieutenant Colonel, U. S. Marine Corps, *A History of the United States Marine Corps*. New York: G. P. Putnam's Sons, 1939.

Mitchell, Donald W., *History of The Modern American Navy*. New York: Alfred A. Knopf, 1946.

Mitchell, William, *Memoirs of World War I*. New York: Random House, 1960.

Moorehead, Alan, *Gallipoli*. New York: Harper & Bros., 1956.

Mortane, Jacques, *The Aces—As Portrayed by Themselves*. Paris: Lemerre et Cie (Librairie Alphonse Lemerre), 1917.

New York Times Current History of the European War, vols. XII, XIII. New York: 1917.

Nutting, Anthony, *Lawrence of Arabia*. New York: Clarkson N. Potter, Inc., Publisher, 1961.

O'Connor, Richard, *Black Jack Pershing*. New York: Doubleday & Co., Inc., 1961.

Oughton, Frederick, *The Aces*. New York: G. P. Putnam's Sons, 1960.

Pershing, John J., *My Experiences in the World War*, 2 vols. New York: Frederick A. Stokes Co., 1931.

*Reiners, Ludwig, *The Lamps Went Out in Europe*. New York: Pantheon Books Inc., 1955.

Reynolds, Quentin, *They Fought For the Sky*. New York: Rinehart & Co., 1957.

Robertson, Bruce, *Air Aces of the 1914–1918 War*. England, Letchworth, Herts.: Harleyford Publications, 1959.

Rommel, Erwin, General Field Marshal, *Infantry Attacks*. Translated by Lt. Col. G. E. Kiddé, U. S. Army. Potsdam: Ludwig Voggenreiter Verlag, 1937; Washington, D.C.: Combat Forces Press, 1956.

Seldes, George, *Sawdust Caesar*. New York: Harper & Brothers, Publishers, 1935.

Simonds, Frank H., *History of the World War*, vols. 4, 5. New York: Doubleday, Page & Co., 1919.

———*They Won the War*. New York: Harper and Brothers, 1931.

Soutar, Andrew, *With Ironside in North Russia*. London: Hutchinson & Co., Ltd., 1940.

*Stamps, Col. T. Dodson, and Esposito, Col. Vincent J., editors, *A Short Military History of World War I*. West Point, N. Y.: 1954.

Terraine, John, *Mons*. New York: The Macmillan Co., 1960.

**The Medal of Honor of the United States Army*. Washington, D.C.: Government Printing Office, 1948.

**The Times History of the War*, vols. 2, 7, 10, 18, 19. London: *The Times*, 1917.

Tompkins, Raymond Sidney, *The Story of the Rainbow Division.* New York: Boni and Liveright, 1919.

Treusch, Horst von Buttlar Brandenfels, *Zeppelins Over England.* New York: Harcourt, Brace & Co., 1932.

Verdun—Illustrated Historical Guide. Editions Lorraines, Frémont (undated).

Vertex, Jean, *Les Carrefours du Haut Merite, La Medaille Militaire.* Paris: Editions Elzevir, 1952.

Welcome to Verdun. (Historical mimeographs) Hdq. 4th Logistical Command, U. S. Army Europe.

Whitehouse, Arthur G. J., *The Years of The Sky Kings.* New York: Doubleday & Co., 1959.

Wolff, Leon, *In Flanders Fields.* New York: The Viking Press, 1958.

INDEX

237

Vladivostok, 213–19
von Kress; *see* Kressenstein

West Point, 128
"White Russians," 218, 220
Whittlesey, Maj. Charles W., 178–85
Wilhelm II, Kaiser, 11–14, 19, 27, 36, 56, 57, 67, 82, 84, 103, 107, 133, 135, 149, 151, 154, 195, 210–11
Wilhelm, Crown Prince, 89, 91, 92, 93, 156, 211
Williams, Capt. Lloyd W., 157
Willis, Capt. Raymond, 66
Wilson, President Woodrow, 16–18, 67, 109, 124, 132, 158, 212, 218, 220, 221–22, 225

Wood, Maj. Gen. Leonard, 127
Woodfill, 1st Lt. Sam, 192–93
Woods, 1st Lt. Joseph, 189

Xeros, Gulf of, 64

"Yanks"; *see* United States Army
York, Sgt. Alvin C., 186–89
"Young Turks," 58, 59
Ypres, 73, 75, 99, 139, 145
Yser Canal, 36

Zeppelin, Count Ferdinand, 81
Zeppelins, 80, 81–85, 148
Zouaves, 36, 38